Galvanic Treatment

BEAUTY GUIDE 3

Galvanic Treatment

Ann Gallant

F.S.H.B.Th., Int.B.Th.Dip., D.R.E. (Tutor),
Teacher's Certificate in Further Education

*Formerly Lecturer Responsible
for Beauty Therapy at
Chichester College of Higher Technology, and
Gloucestershire College of Art and Technology*

Stanley Thornes (Publishers) Ltd

First published in 1985 by
Stanley Thornes (Publishers) Ltd,
Old Station Drive,
Leckhampton,
CHELTENHAM GL53 0DN

British Library Cataloguing in Publication Data

Gallant, Ann
    Galvanic treatments.—(Beauty guides; 3)
    1. Skin—Care and hygiene   2. Beauty culture
    I. Title   II. Series
    646.7'26'088042   RL87

ISBN 0-85950-215-5

Typeset in 10/11 Garamond
by Tech-Set, Gateshead, Tyne & Wear.
Printed and bound in Great Britain
at The Bath Press, Avon.

Contents

Acknowledgements

My thanks go to my husband, Robin Cleugh, who worked with patience and skill to provide all the photographs in this practical guide — making it so much more usable to the beauty practitioner working in the field. Thanks also to Angela Lumley for her care in the line drawings and sympathetic approach to the subject.

For my daughter Patsy's forbearance in acting as a model for the photographs, I'd like to record a special mother's appreciation.

1

The galvanic system

USES OF GALVANISM

The use of galvanic current in beauty therapy provides a very useful and effective means for the therapist to both deep-cleanse the skin — *desincrustation* — and introduce active substances into it for specific effect — *iontophoresis* — also known as *ionization.*

Desincrustation uses the galvanic current in combination with a dissolving type of soap-based substance with an alkaline pH (over the pH of 7), to deep-cleanse or flush the skin freeing it gradually from trapped waste matter. The term desincrustation comes from the Latin word *des* — to undo — and from *incrustation* — crustations or surface build-up, oily blockage, skin debris, etc. Desincrustation is said des-in-crust-ation.

Iontophoresis or ionization is a process where galvanic current is used to pass active substances through the intact skin, where once penetrated, they remain effectively working in the skin's deeper layers until gradually absorbed by the body. The term iontophoresis comes from the Greek word *ion* — to wander. Iontophoresis is said i-on-toe-for-resis.

HOW IT WORKS

The active substances cross the skin barrier on a galvanic charge, with the current flowing through the skin's surface forming a link between the two applicators used. The client and her skin offer *resistance* to this flow of *constant direct current* (DC), in a form which is measured on the equipment as units of milliamps — thousandths of an amp. The texture of the skin, its moisture content, oil level, the amount of scar tissue present, its sensitivity, etc., will all alter the sensation the client will experience while the treatment is in progress, both for desincrustation and iontophoresis. These factors will also alter the skin resistance level registering on the milliamp meter. When the applicators are in position, the client's body acts to complete the circuit, its resistance giving a reading on the meter.

PRODUCTS FOR CLINIC
AND HOME USE

Active ampoules and Aqua *products for clinic and home use*

The galvanic current is able to achieve penetration of active substances through the skin's normally very effective barrier mechanisms by the attraction of the ions — electrically charged elements in the substances used in ampoule form within galvanic treatment. The molecules of the substances assume either negative or positive electrical charges in the preparation process in the cosmetic laboratory, and for this reason are in sealed glass ampoules, to retain electrical activity and ensure the freshness and biological activity of the ingredients. The pH level of the substance, its acidity or alkalinity, also directly relates to the electrical charge with which it will be applied, and the effect it is likely to create.

ACTION OF ACTIVE IONS
INTO THE SKIN

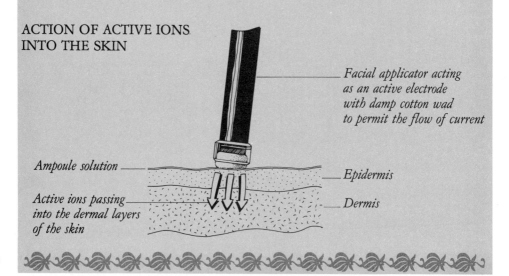

Facial applicator acting as an active electrode with damp cotton wad to permit the flow of current

Ampoule solution

Active ions passing into the dermal layers of the skin

Epidermis

Dermis

THE BEAUTY GALLERY GALVANIC UNIT

The galvanic unit has an on/off switch which also acts as a pilot light to warn when the unit is switched on, an intensity control which also determines the direction of the current, either *negative* or *positive,* and a milliamp meter to show the level of skin resistance and indicate the amount of galvanic current being used. The intensity control, which also determines the polarity, has for reasons of safety to be turned back through the zero position before the polarity can be changed. The unit has outlets for facial and body applicators. This enables the one unit to be used for a full range of facial and body treatments, including cellulite treatments which extend its range of applications considerably. Sufficient capacity has been built into the unit to enable several pads to be used together for treating cellulite problems with iontophoresis and anti-cellulite products, a facility not normally available on a basic facial galvanic machine.

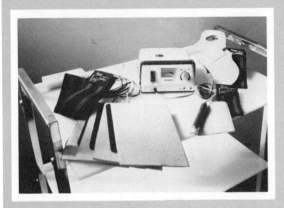

GALVANIC UNIT, WAND, MASK, ENVELOPES AND ELECTRODE

Applicators for facial applications include a facial 'wand' designed to give easier handling and greater control, with a more pleasant feel for the client, and a full face mask to provide a very even spread of galvanic current over the area of treatment. Both applicators can be used for desincrustation and iontophoresis methods. These are considered the active or working applicators or electrodes. The circuit is completed by an indifferent applicator or electrode which is strapped firmly around the client's arm to form a good contact area. This is termed the non-working electrode, more accurately the *indifferent* electrode. All electrodes are attached to the galvanic unit by leads. The working surfaces of the applicators have to be covered by some material that will retain moisture. Special disposable wads are used with the wand, while the indifferent electrode is placed within a special damp fabric-type envelope to protect the skin and form a good flow transmission.

No metal parts must be exposed on the applicators where they come into skin contact, and the client must remove all metal jewellery prior to the galvanic application, as it can become blackened by the action of the current.

All surfaces in contact with the client must be moist if the galvanic current is to flow. *Without moisture there can be no flow transmission between the electrodes and the circuit is not complete.* So the skin itself, the applicator protection, wad, etc., plus the special envelopes themselves, must all be moist to get a good, comfortable, effective flow of current.

GALVANIC TREATMENT

Treatment in progress with the facial applicator and indifferent pad in use

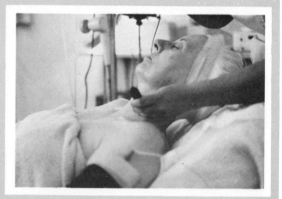

GALVANIC ELECTRODES/APPLICATORS

When setting up galvanic treatment for a client, there must be at least two electrodes or applicators in use and moisture must be present to allow for the flow of galvanic current. These electrodes are called *poles* and act to attract or repel the actively charged elements or ions in the desincrustation or iontophoresis fluids.

Most galvanic machines (including the *Beauty Gallery* units) have fixed polarities; the *red lead is the positive electrode connection* and the *black lead is the negative electrode connection.* When applying *negative* polarity (the one most commonly used) the *red* lead will be on the *indifferent arm pad* and the *black* lead or leads (for face mask or rollers) will go to the *working applicator.* The treatment will then start correctly and there will be no confusion. With the *Beauty Gallery* applicators, each method of application has its own complete set of leads to save the therapist time and anxiety.

When the polarity is reversed to *positive* on the machine, the leads obviously can't change colour to match, but the desired effect will still be achieved; the indifferent arm electrode will become a negative pole, attracting the opposite positive elements on a positive charge. Remember, the leads are only wires that carry current and the electrode on the arm is only a conductive pad, the two only become effective when the polarity is set by the therapist and current is provided by the galvanic machine.

As manufacturers around the world use different colours for their leads, it is important for therapists to check exactly which colour lead is acting as the positive connection at the start of treatment. This is normally a red lead (on the indifferent pad at the start of treatment), with the working electrode connections given either a black, green or white lead. As the polarity is fixed within the unit, therapists have to confirm this point before they begin work with the system. Simply follow the guidance given by the manufacturer to avoid errors in use.

The *negative pole* is the *penetrating pole* and indeed most ampoules will require a negative polarity (thus the machine's polarity control must be turned to negative to match the ampoule instructions). This indicates that the ampoule contains negative elements (or has an alkaline pH) that are attracted to the opposite — *positive* — pole, which is the electrode on the arm. The active lotion will penetrate and be drawn into the skin, attracted by the 'magnetism' effect of the opposite pole, as soon as the working electrode has passed over it. Many ampoules are marked *Negative to Positive* (including *Ann Gallant* ampoules) which simply means starting treatment on the negative pole, completing the penetration on this more comfortable polarity, and concluding on the positive pole *if necessary* to give a more stimulating, skin tightening effect to the application. The positive polarity application can be left out if this action is not needed or does not seem suitable for the skin, and the entire application given to the negative polarity. The therapist can, if she chooses, use the special effects of the different poles to help her in her work. Alternatively, she can work mainly with the negative pole, concentrating on its penetration action on the active lotions in the ampoules or using it within desincrustation.

Ampoules containing colloidal substances (collagen) benefit if given equal time to first the negative then the positive polarity (normally on a lower intensity/skin resistance level). This is because the substances have molecules which do not migrate or move in a definite direction, so they need both polarities to gain maximum penetration and action in the skin. As the skin types which will gain maximum benefit from the action of collagen are also in the more mature age range, the toning and tightening action of the positive pole is a bonus in treatment helping delay skin softening and crepey texture.

With *desincrustation, which is always applied on a negative charge,* active substances previously placed on the wet skin will be attracted to the opposite polarity of the arm electrode. The desincrustation fluid — a soapy, oil-dissolving type of formulation with *ion activity* (electrical activity) encaptured by the glass phial ampoule —

cannot pass through the skin, but is drawn deeply into it. The desincrustation sequence uses the electrically active product — that is, the desincrustation ampoule — plus the effects of the galvanic current to break up the oily surface layer; applying the facial applicator with disposable cotton wads to remove the soiled matter. The negative charge of the galvanic current attempts to draw the product into the skin, towards the positive pole of the arm electrode, but the oily surface matter blocks this action and this skin resistance registers on the galvanic machine's meter, guiding the therapist. With desincrustation, a deep-cleansing, flushing and dissolving effect is achieved on the oily waste and debris that coat and block the surface of the skin, filling follicles and giving an oily, blocked appearance. The oily matter and dead skin on the *stratum corneum* (surface epidermal layer) is broken down and following the conclusion of the application is rinsed away very thoroughly. Desincrustation is a cleansing procedure applied early in the treatment routine: it is always applied on a negative charge and then rinsed away. Treatment is applied with the *red* lead going to the *indifferent arm pad* and the *black* lead going to the *facial 'wand' applicator*.

For *iontophoresis*, where actual penetration of the pure substances into the skin is required, the indifferent electrode is again the attracting force and can be designated on the machine to act either as a negative or positive pole simply by altering the polarity. The electrodes used are the same as for desincrustation, but the action is different. The ampoule's contents now pass right through the skin's surface layers. A facial wand applicator can be used with its moist cotton wad, or a facial mask or rollers can be employed (both of these have two black leads). The indifferent pad on the arm with its red lead is applied as usual, even though there are two black leads going to a mask or roller applicator (these two black leads simply share the current and allow good distribution over a wider area). *Don't forget*, whatever applicator is in use, the indifferent pad is *always* needed for it completes the circuit and allows the flow to take place.

Most penetration is completed on a negative pole, this being the most effective method for client comfort. The positive pole, however, has special actions and can be used effectively if applied with care. The positive pole has a more toning and tightening effect on the skin, which can be useful on ageing skin or one losing its firmness. Certain ampoules are formulated to pass through the skin on a positive charge because of the pH of their ingredients. If chosen to act as a positive pole the indifferent electrode will attract the negative elements in the ampoule's substance, and the ampoule will be marked as needing a negative

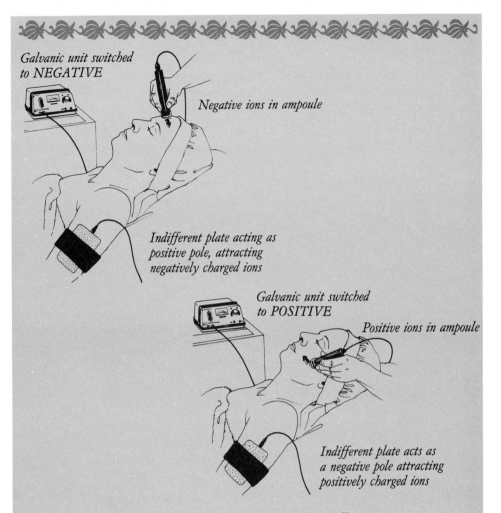

Galvanic unit switched to NEGATIVE

Negative ions in ampoule

Indifferent plate acting as positive pole, attracting negatively charged ions

Galvanic unit switched to POSITIVE

Positive ions in ampoule

Indifferent plate acts as a negative pole attracting positively charged ions

charge (−) minus. If chosen to act as a negative pole it will attract the positive elements in the ampoule, and this will be marked as needing a positive charge (+) plus.

So it is only necessary to follow the instructions given on the ampoules: if marked negative (−), they are used on a negative charge; if marked positive (+), they need a positive polarity set on the machine.

GALVANIC APPLICATION

All galvanic effects are based on either the deep-cleansing or penetration process, often commonly referred to as *galvanic ionization,* simply meaning the use of active ions or electrically charged elements in treatment. If both these processes are considered more carefully and their application noted, then it will be evident what a useful factor they are in professional therapy.

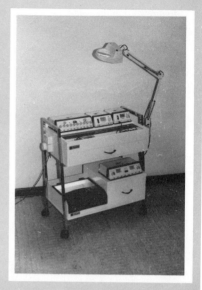

CONTRA-INDICATIONS

There are some clients who are not suitable for galvanic treatment, that is they are termed *contra-indicated*. If a client is of a highly nervous disposition, it should not be applied on a first visit but can be introduced at a later stage if really needed by the skin. Galvanic treatments are not advisable over very vascular skin, or in the case of body cellulite not over varicose veins. Clients with a history of nervous disorders, or who have suffered damage to the nervous system (pinched nerves, paralysis of a nerve, etc.) are also contra-indicated to cellulite body treatments. Open skin, rashes and isolated blemishes should be avoided as the treatment would be uncomfortable and could aggravate the problem. If during treatment the client experiences severe discomfort on the skin then the treatment should be concluded, by reducing the intensity smoothly back to zero. The reason for the problem can be investigated, and if it relates to poor skin preparation, this can then be rectified.

There will always be some skins that appear to present no visible contra-indications, but which in the application prove to be contra-indicated because of sensitivity. For this reason it is essential to talk to the client during the application to assess her reactions, and receive feedback from her regarding the sensation she is experiencing.

Galvanic applications are active and effective in their results, and so are likely to cause the occasional reaction within the client. The therapist must simply be on the alert and will then find no problems occurring which cannot be overcome.

GALVANIC UNIT APPLICATORS

(a)

(b)

General conditions which affect the body need to be considered. If the client is on the 'loop' for contraception purposes, medical permission would be advisable. Pregnancy at all stages is a contra-indication. Metal bridge work in teeth and metal implants anywhere in the body require adjustment of the application. If in any doubt about the advisability of application, ask the client to seek medical guidance.

2

Desincrustation

APPLICATION

For the detailed deep-cleansing of the skin by galvanic desincrustation the skin is first cleansed thoroughly by cosmetic measures,
and then the indifferent electrode is connected to the client, and
the active working electrode prepared according to type. The
indifferent electrode is a rubber pad incorporating conductive

CONTROLS AND THEIR USE

*(a) Negative and positive polarity/
intensity control, milliamp meter. On-
off switch/pilot light, outlets for
electrodes: face (1), body (2). Connection leads: Red = Positive, Black =
Negative.*

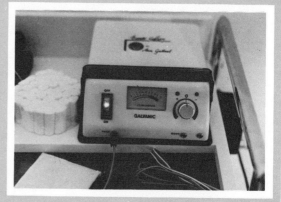

*(b) All applicators must be well
connected and moist when in skin
contact*

'BEAUTY GALLERY' GALVANIC WAND APPLICATOR

(a)

(a), (b) To prepare the facial applicator, moisten cotton wad, hold ends together, place in the clear collar of the applicator, press firmly

(b)

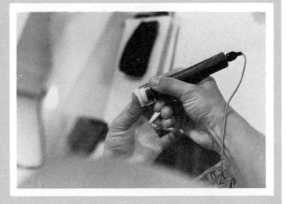

(c) Disposable wads can be changed frequently during desincrustation for an effective and hygenic treatment

material to make it a good electrical contact, covered by a damp sponge envelope attached to the arm by straps. As long as the area of connection is adequate, and the contact firm, then an adequate flow transmission can take place. For safety reasons it is now more normal for arm pads to be used instead of hand-held metal rods, as they allow a larger area of connection, are tightly strapped to the arm forming a closer connection, and cannot break contact with the client as in the case of a hand-held rod, if the client lets go in the middle of the application.

The working electrode or applicator wand is prepared, its special wads moistened and fitted into the perspex ring to make firm and stable contact when in use.

The client's metal jewellery is removed, including rings, etc., which are not in the immediate area of treatment but which will be affected by the galvanic current.

The skin is moistened and an ampoule of desincrustation fluid applied. The working electrode is placed on the skin, the polarity is chosen on the galvanic unit (always a negative charge) and the moisture in the cotton wool covering improves the flow transmission and makes the desincrustation fluid foam.

FIRM CONTACT

Firm contact and a moist surface permits a comfortable treatment, that the client can enjoy

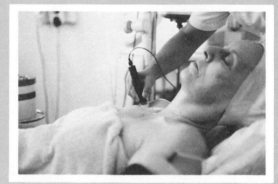

APPLICATION OF THE DESINCRUSTATION FLUID

Apply either directly from the ampoule into the hand or from a small bowl, taking care not to drip solution on the client

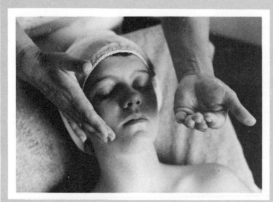

The intensity control can be increased gradually and for a few seconds the galvanic current has to overcome the skin resistance in the area, and very little sensation will be experienced. As the skin resistance lowers in the area the client will become more aware of the sensation, then the intensity control can be adjusted until the client feels a slight prickling sensation. Circular or stroking movements, smoothly applied, are used to create the desired effect gently, and aid the skin-freeing process. *Skin contact should be retained throughout the application* — the wand should not be lifted from the skin and then replaced as this will cause discomfort.

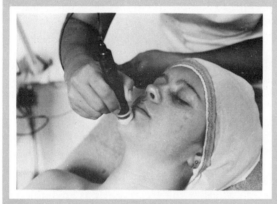

USE OF THE FACIAL APPLICATOR

Use circular movements, to aid skin blockage removal

As soon as the application settles down to a comfortable level — which will vary considerably according to skin sensitivity, moisture, skin irregularities, etc., present — then the treatment should proceed for 4 to 5 minutes, longer if needed, until the skin is pink and has an increased skin temperature. The skin resistance registering on the milliamp meter will show how the galvanic current is affecting the skin, and by talking to the client the therapist is able to judge how the treatment is going. After a few minutes the client may experience a metallic taste in the mouth,

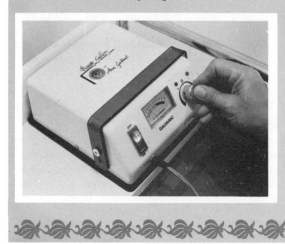

ADJUSTING THE GALVANIC CURRENT

Adjust to the client's tolerance and skin resistance

due to changes in the saliva caused by the current, and this should be explained to her to avoid any anxiety. This should not be unpleasant if the application is being performed at a low level of intensity, for it has been noted that a high level of intensity is not required to make the application effective, simply to allow a good flow transmission between the electrodes. Too strong a metallic taste in the mouth indicates the intensity is too high and must be reduced.

All areas needing the desincrustation effect can be treated, with concentration on the blocked or open-pored areas needing the most help. Open blemishes should not be worked over, but if isolated can be simply avoided in the treatment. This is because the moisture present in these open areas will cause a direct contact, increasing the flow of the current as the area has little skin resistance. This would be unpleasantly smarting for the client, and would make her jump. Likewise any boil-like eruptions, where infection from a follicle problem (folliculitis) has developed into a secondary infection of the surrounding tissues, should be worked around or left alone entirely for the client's comfort. As desincrustation is such a valuable process for the blocked or troubled skin, the skilled therapist must use her own discretion about when a treatment application would be beneficial, and knowing her client's reactions and capacity for galvanic routines would be able to decide whether the treatment was advisable at that time. If the troubled skin is really painful in some areas, it is obviously contra-indicated.

The applicator wand can be applied slowly, which improves the flow of the galvanic current, improving client comfort, or it can be used in a concentrated fashion by working deeply in a circular manner into the nostril folds, up the sides of the nose, between the brows, etc., where the sebaceous glands and their blockage are worst.

Changes in the area of the electrode in contact with the skin change the sensation experienced, so therapists must keep closely in touch with their clients and lower the intensity — and thereby the skin resistance recorded on the milliamp meter — to match the client's comfort. Sometimes one area of the face proves more sensitive than others, perhaps due to healing still taking place in the skin's deeper layers, or an old injury which has left the skin sensitive in that area.

The larger area of skin contact involved with the 'wand' applicator makes the application much more pleasant for the client, as it does not concentrate the galvanic current but spreads it evenly over an area. As client acceptance is a vital factor in getting the individual to accept the treatment, this is a very important point. Clients will not have desincrustation — however good for their skins it is — if it

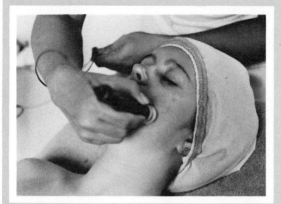

POINTS OF TECHNIQUE

(a) Use firm but gentle circular movements

(b) Concentrated work on the centre of the face

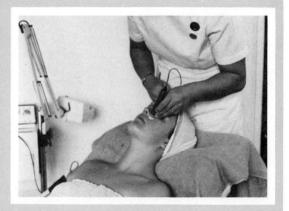

(c) Sweeping movements on the cheek and jaw-line area

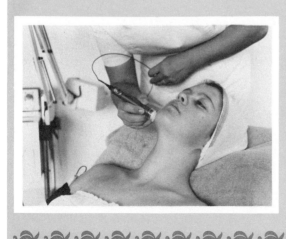

(d) Application of the ampoule, with light massage movements

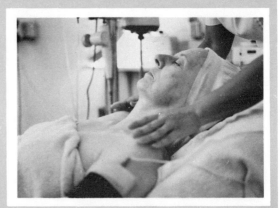

(e) Use even slow strokes with the facial applicator

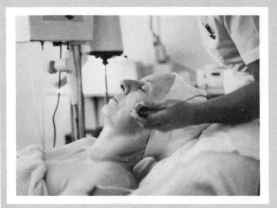

(f) The ampoule quickly penetrates the skin under the galvanic current

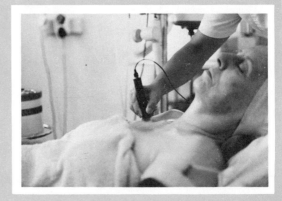

is painful to have applied. On the *Beauty Gallery* galvanic system, the controls are designed to permit a slow build-up, helping client comfort/acceptance.

Likewise the full face mask which is mainly used for ionization of the active or corrective ampoules, can be used for desincrustation, though in this case there is not the additional action of the circular movements to loosen the surface blockage, and all areas of the face receive the same amount of desincrustation action. To maintain the cleansing effect on a skin that is becoming a little sensitive, however, it is a useful alternative approach. In this case the mask must be lined for hygiene purposes with a moist tissue-paper mask liner, or damp gauze cut to shape, and with holes cut for eyes, nose and mouth. This allows the desincrustation to take place but acts as a barrier between the skin and the mask itself. As the action of the desincrustation will be much more evenly spread over the whole facial area, a longer application time might be needed, with the treatment given on a low intensity. However, as all the areas of the face are receiving identical treatment, not spasmodically as with a 'wand'-type applicator, it may be found that very similar effects are produced within the normal 4 to 5 minutes' application time. The sequence of application starts with two straps being placed behind the head, and the indifferent plate attached to the arm. The ampoule is applied, prepared mask liner or gauze placed on the skin, the *two* active plates attached to the mask, the mask is applied and held in place by the straps.

When desincrustation is complete, by whichever method, the intensity can be reduced smoothly and steadily back to zero, and the active electrode removed from the skin. The galvanic unit may then be turned off, and the indifferent electrode removed if the client is not to receive any further galvanic application within the routine. If iontophoresis is to follow at a later stage, perhaps concluding the treatment, then the arm-strapped electrode can remain in place — which saves time and fuss for the client. However it should always be checked for moisture just prior to the application, to ensure it is damp enough to make good contact.

Small concentrated circular movements are used to help free skin blockage, and allow the desincrustation process to be fully effective. Then the skin is rinsed very thoroughly to remove all the skin debris, using just moist cotton-wool pads or clean, well-wrung foam sponges. Avoid rinsing the sponges in dirty water; rather, use several sponges and put them aside as they become soiled. This rinsing and removal of the skin's wastes should be carried out meticulously, as it alters the success of the subsequent applications in the treatment if the skin is not well prepared and soapy matter remains in the skin's tissues. The skin can then be examined under a magnifying light to see progress and decide further treatment. It will also then be apparent as to whether iontophoresis with a corrective ampoule would be beneficial to normalize the skin and improve skin functioning. Special ampoules for seborrhoea or open pores could be used at a later stage in the treatment, normally concluding the treatment so that the active substance remains in the skin.

REMOVAL OF AMPOULE
WITH SPONGES

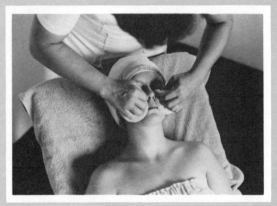

INDICATIONS FOR DESINCRUSTATION

All but the most blemished, hypersensitive, extremely dehydrated or mature skins can benefit from some form of desincrustation used to different degrees. This is because the deep-cleansing it provides prepares the skin so well for effective and active routines, which would not normally find the skin so receptive and able to benefit from the combinations of massage products and electrical therapy.

For the blocked skin, it is perhaps the most effective application the professional therapist has to offer the client in her quest for a clear untroubled skin.

3

Iontophoresis

APPLICATION

Iontophoresis — the passing of active substances through the skin on a galvanic charge — is normally carried out at the conclusion of a facial treatment routine, so that the active elements stay within the skin to carry on their work following the treatment. However this is not always the case, and ionization can be carried out at any stage of the treatment routine as long as the skin is really clean, does not have any oily film on it, and as long as active routines such as direct high frequency, drying masks, etc. *do not follow* the galvanic iontophoresis application and alter its effectiveness.

For the fact is that once the contents of the ampoule are passed by the galvanic current into the skin they are there to stay. Only gradually are they absorbed into the blood stream, through the interchange of blood and tissue fluids which takes place in the skin's subcutaneous layers. Naturally massage speeds this process, and for this reason many therapists feel it preferable to conclude with iontophoresis, providing the skin with the maximum chance to benefit from the ampoule used.

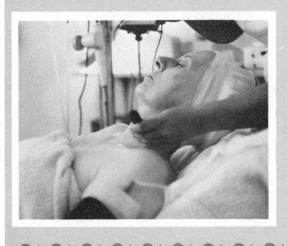

GALVANIC TREATMENT
IN PROGRESS

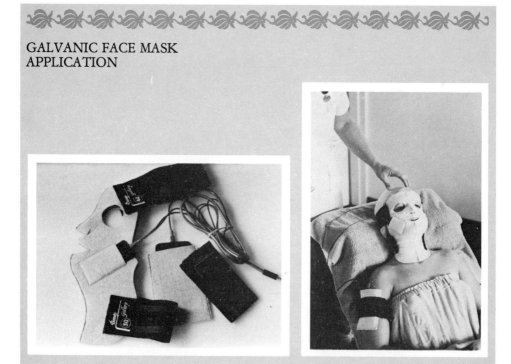

So iontophoresis could be applied prior to massage immediately following the skin cleansing, or more normally concluding the facial treatment at the end of the routine.

The indifferent electrode and active electrode are prepared as for desincrustation. The full face mask may be chosen for the penetration of the active substances, as it provides a comfortable and even flow transmission of the galvanic current and ensures all areas of the face receive identical periods of ionization, or the facial wand can be used to allow different areas of the face to receive different levels of treatment. (Liner papers or fine gauze cut to shape and moistened are once again used with the mask.)

The chosen ampoule is applied to the skin, gently massaged in with the finger tips on to a slightly damp skin, perhaps following the use of compresses or vapour steaming. This aids the penetration and makes the skin more receptive. The polarity of the ampoules is indicated on the box, and *this indicates the polarity to be chosen on the galvanic unit.* Some ampoules require a positive charge, some a negative charge, and some contain active elements requiring both negative and positive charges. In this case, first negative polarity is used, the intensity returned to zero, and then the application of the positive polarity follows. On all *Beauty Gallery* galvanic units it is necessary to pass through the zero point of the polarity changer in order to change to the opposite polarity.

This is a very safe point in the application of the galvanic technique and prevents accidents occurring, which could cause the client discomfort, if the polarity was altered while the intensity was at a working level.

Once again the skin will react differently depending on sensitivity, etc., and the client can give guidance to the therapist as to sensation. It is not necessary for the galvanic current to be used at a high intensity to permit the substance to pass into the skin; as long as the flow transmission is good, and the indifferent and active electrodes are in good contact, well moistened, etc., then the required effect is achieved. If the mask is not damp enough, or not in tight skin contact, then the galvanic current flow cannot occur even with the magnetic effect exerted by the attraction of the opposite pole or electrode. If it does not make contact, it cannot work. Once contact is made, it cannot help but work, even when used on the most minute skin resistance level.

So very low levels of skin resistance can be recorded on the meter and the treatment will be working well. The client can be given the benefit of feeling the slightest prickling sensation to involve her in the routine, and she may experience a slight metallic taste in the mouth due to changes in the saliva. These changes must be explained to her to avoid any anxiety, and to confirm to her that the substances are passing into her skin effectively. Then the level of intensity can be reduced slightly as it is not necessary for the client to feel anything for the treatment to be working, and this reduces the metallic taste. Galvanic treatments can be completely applied below the client's perception level, that is, at a level at which it is not discernible or felt. The fact that the treatments are being effective will be evident to the client after only a few applications, due to visible changes in the skin's texture, colour, elasticity and overall appearance.

A few minutes only is required to pass the contents of the ampoule into the skin. Therapists should understand this point and not feel they must follow the ampoule instructions exactly as specified on the box, but rather, use them for guidance only. The iontophoresis procedure is normally complete in itself if used as a conclusion of the routine, and is never rinsed away from the skin. The skin is usually very matt, taut and attractive after ampoule therapy, so ideally it should be left free from make-up, and only eye make-up and lipstick applied. However, as the ampoule has passed completely into the skin, and will continue its action whatever happens, there is no real reason why the client should not be made up if she prefers, and it makes her feel better. This after all is the point of treatment.

FACIAL MASK APPLICATION

(a) Head straps and indifferent arm pad applied

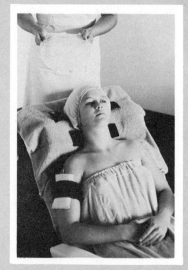

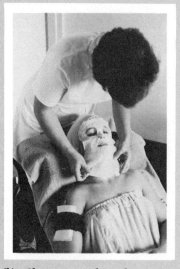

(b) Chosen ampoule and wet gauze liner are applied. Prepare damp facial mask with two electrodes, applied and adjusted to client's comfort

(c)

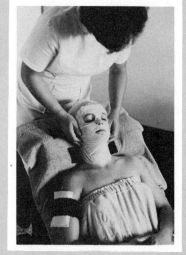

(d)

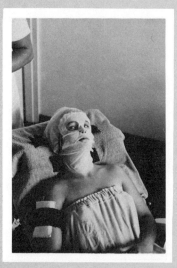

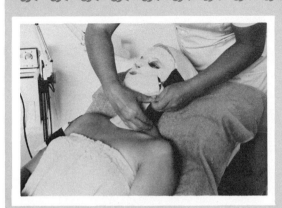

(e) Quickly ease the mask to fit really snugly around the jaw-line and neck areas

(f) Make sure eye, lip and nostril holes fit and client is comfortable

(g) Stay with the client throughout the treatment to avoid anxiety and ensure good results

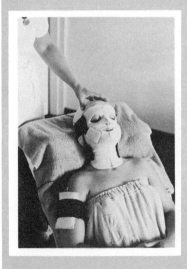

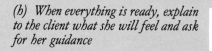

(h) When everything is ready, explain to the client what she will feel and ask for her guidance

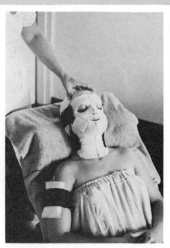

(i) Adjust the intensity/skin resistance levels according to the client's reactions. Involve her in the treatment

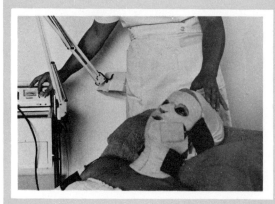

(j) Complete the treatment on negative, or negative and positive poles if needed, return to zero, switch off

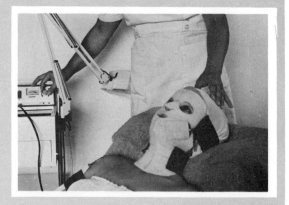

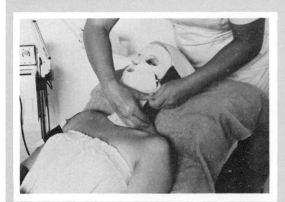

(k) *Quickly release her from the mask straps and leads*

(l)

(m) *Remove liner mask — DON'T rinse the skin, leave the ampoule to do its work. Apply moisture protection if needed*

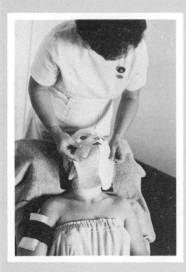

4

Ampoules and polarity

The ampoules are carefully prepared and marked with positive (+) or negative (−) polarity, and will also indicate their pH (acidity or alkalinity). The polarity may be marked on each individual ampoule, or more commonly on the box of 10 ampoules. So it is important not to get them muddled up, otherwise it will be impossible to know which polarity they need. They are presented as individual glass ampoules in order not to lose the electrically

AMPOULES

(a) Ampoules are available to meet a wide range of skin conditions

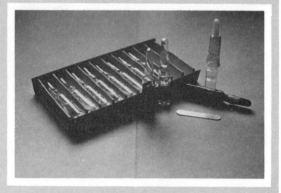

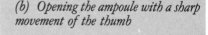

(b) Opening the ampoule with a sharp movement of the thumb

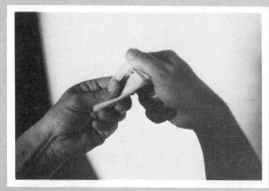

(c) Sawing across the line indicated with the blade provided

charged capacity which enables the contents to flow through the skin. The ampoules are opened just prior to application, either broken open or using the small blade provided along the line indicated, with a sawing movement. The entire contents of each ampoule are used within the treatment if the skin will accept the solution. The electrically charged ions do not retain their activity for an extended period, so it is better to try to get the skin to take all of the active solution if possible.

If all the solution will not be absorbed by the skin during treatment, the ampoule can be sealed with cotton wool and sellotape, and be given to the client to be used at home while its properties are still ion active and the contents pure.

Iontophoresis ampoules and desincrustation ampoules have quite different purposes; those intended for desincrustation are rinsed away after the application, having done their work, while those used for iontophoresis are left in the skin, still having their work to do.

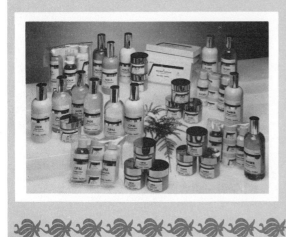

(d) Ampoules work best when used with a treatment range such as Gallery Line, *for clinic and home use*

ACIDITY/ALKALINITY OR THE pH
OF AMPOULES

Sometimes the pH of the substance is shown instead of the polarity, and this also provides the necessary guidance for practical use.

In acidic solutions (pH below 7) the amino acid will be present as a positive (+) ion, the molecules will have a positive (+) charge and are used on a positive (+) polarity, as they are attracted to the negative pole when the solution is charged electrically.

In alkaline solutions (pH above 7) the amino acid will be present as a negative (−) ion, the molecules will have a negative (−) charge and are used on a negative (−) polarity on the machine, as they are attracted to the positive pole when the solution is charged.

POLARITY

The polarity of the ampoule and the polarity chosen on the machine are always the same. Positive (+) ampoules are charged on a positive (+) polarity, and negative (−) ampoules are charged on a negative (−) polarity. What can alter is the polarity of the electrode, acting as the attracting pole to the actively charged molecules in the liquid of the ampoule. The indifferent (non-working) electrode on the arm, can be a negative or positive pole. This provides the electrical flow transmission *link* of the galvanic current without which it would not be operative — and acts as a magnet-like force to either negatively or positively charged substances.

Remember that it is only by determining the polarity on the machine's switch, that it is decided which ions in the substances will flow, attracted to the opposite polarity. According to their pH and the polarity of the ions, ampoules will either penetrate through ionization on a negative charge, that is the machine switched to negative (−) polarity and the indifferent non-working electrode acting as the attracting positive pole, or if the ampoules are prepared in such a way as to go through the skin on a positive (+) charge then the machine dials are placed on the positive (+) polarity (to match the ampoule), and the indifferent plate acts as the attracting negative polarity.

So it is not the electrode plate *itself* which has a polarity, it is only the polarity *given to it* by choosing on the galvanic machine the polarity or action needed for the specific substance.

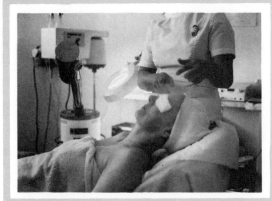

IONTOPHORESIS — USING THE FACIAL WAND APPLICATION METHOD

(a) Preparing the skin well with vapour, helps the flow transmission, and reduces skin resistance

(b) Choose and apply the ampoule with care, taking special note of existing problems

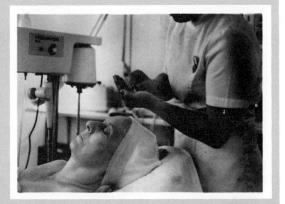

(c) Special attention can be given to areas of greatest need, especially in the mature woman

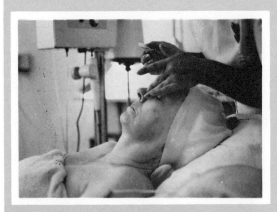

(d) Apply the ampoule with light massage movements

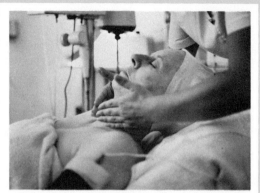

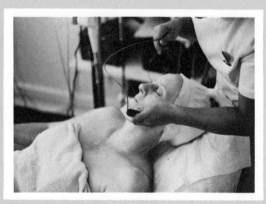

(e) Use even slow strokes with the facial applicator

(f)

(f)–(h) The ampoule quickly penetrates the skin under the galvanic current

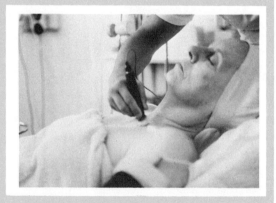

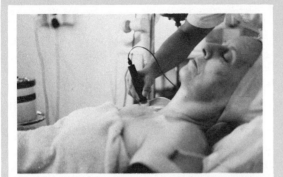

(g)

(h)

DEEP-CLEANSING/DESINCRUSTATION

When unwanted oily blockage in the follicles, waste matter, etc., is to be ejected from the skin, the working electrode cleans and frees the compacted seborrhoeic layer on the surface which causes the blocked pores, blackheads, and pustular blemishes. Part of the action is the rather caustic effect of the desincrustation solution on the oily matter, but mainly it is the flow of the galvanic current which combines to form a breaking up or a lysing action on the surface layers of oil or grime. This deep-cleansing effect can be achieved very gently, with only the smallest amount of skin resistance registering on the milliamp meter, with the sensation only just discernible by the client as a slight prickling on the skin. Desincrustation is applied on a negative charge.

CATIONS AND ANIONS

Ions with a positive charge are called *cations* because they are attracted by the cathode or negative pole.

Ions with a negative charge are called *anions* since they are attracted by the anode or positive pole.

When parts of cells (atoms) carry an electrical charge they are called ions and they become attracted to the opposite polarity. As ion is from the Greek verb 'to wander', it becomes clear that these ions can travel with an electrical current. They simply use the current to link them up and enable them to pass through the intact skin. The current is the vehicle which makes the flow possible.

The opposite polarity which attracts the ions is the most important factor; the galvanic current is simply the link mechanism which allows it to happen, provided good contacts are made to permit excellent flow transmission. Factors for good contact include wet coverings for the electrodes, firm strapping of the electrodes against the skin, or firm and even contact with the working electrodes, plus good skin preparation — the skin must be clean and moist.

The galvanic current can of course also pass distilled water through the skin, as long as its ions are still present (it is not de-ionized). This creates an interchange of tissue fluids in the cell membranes, helping to hydrate and stimulate the circulation, but it has no other curative, normalizing or regenerative actions as would be present if ampoules were applied.

Many electrically charged ions flow with the electrical current, like pebbles in a stream moved along by the activity of the current flow direction. When the galvanic treatment is applied with ionization on a negative charge, the negative ions are flowing with the current, towards the attraction of the positive electrode. Here the ions flow with the direction of the current.

THE INDIFFERENT ELECTRODE ACTING AS EITHER
A NEGATIVE OR POSITIVE POLE

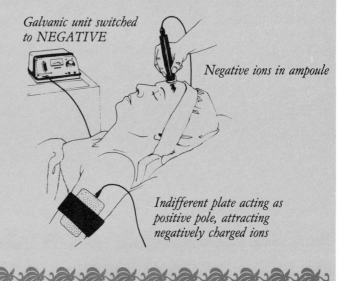

Galvanic unit switched to NEGATIVE

Negative ions in ampoule

Indifferent plate acting as positive pole, attracting negatively charged ions

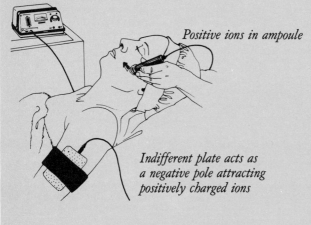

Galvanic unit switched to POSITIVE

Positive ions in ampoule

Indifferent plate acts as a negative pole attracting positively charged ions

FLOW TRANSMISSION

The attraction of the opposite polarity chosen on the machine acts to draw the active substances into the surface skin, on the flow of the galvanic current. Only a tiny amount of current is required to accomplish this flow process, and bring the active elements into the subcutaneous skin layers where they can be most effective. This level is well below that at which the client is aware of any sensation, but in order that she should feel that an effect is being created, it is satisfactory to progress to the level of skin resistance where the client starts to be aware of slight skin prickling. Then at this point turn down the intensity slightly, perhaps reduce by one milliamp of resistance, and progress with the application.

If it is understood that correctly applied, there is no way the actively charged ions in the active solutions in the ampoules can do anything else but flow into the skin on the attraction of the opposite polarity, it will be understood why a high intensity is unnecessary to make the treatment effective. The lotions are not pushed into the skin, they are *pulled* in, drawn as inevitably as metal pins are drawn to a magnet.

Even when the skin offers resistance to the galvanic current, perhaps because of keratinized (horny) scar tissue, excessive seborrhoea, etc., and the client cannot feel the prickling sensation, the treatment will still be working effectively, even on the very lowest intensity/lowest skin resistance on the meter. The active substances will be passing through the intact skin barrier with ease.

CLIENT SENSATION

The only reason why the client should be allowed to feel any sensation is because this appears to involve her in the treatment, and confirms for her its effectiveness. This shows her that something is happening and encourages her in her treatment efforts. A level of feedback from the client is desirable as to the sensations experienced, as this guides the therapist as to how the application is progressing, and avoids the risks of skin irritation, etc. The client should only experience a slight skin prickling, and after a few minutes, a slight metallic taste in the mouth due to changes in the saliva.

This conversation or feedback from the client is essential, as some individuals experience a skin sensation with no intensity at all being used, with the skin resistance registering at almost nil. This may be due to previous over-treatment by which the skin has become over-sensitized, and reacts fiercely. Reasons for this are many and include reaction to bio-peeling, over-strong cleansing measures, abrasive peels, all strongly effective measures designed to remove surface oil and dead skin. So the skin is actually physically thinner, and much more susceptible to reactions from treatment products and procedures, especially electrical routines such as desincrustation and ionization or penetration of products. The galvanic current then has very little skin resistance to overcome, and can bring about an immediate reaction on the skin, instant erythema (error-theme-a). The client is also immediately aware of skin prickling, which may be uncomfortable.

So for whatever reason, the client's reaction is the best guidance to use as to intensity or skin resistance level desirable. Also for the length of the application, the erythema (skin reddening) and increased skin temperature provide the best guidance as to when the skin has had enough treatment.

Instructions as to meter readings, length of application, etc., often printed on the box of ampoules only serve to *guide* the therapist, not dictate to her how the treatment must be given. *For only she has in front of her the client,* her skin condition, texture, sensitivity, etc., and only she can gain from the client the reaction experienced, and see for herself how the skin is responding, reacting or over-reacting.

If therapists use their common sense they will see that it would be impossible for it to be predetermined on the ampoule instructions as to what is the most suitable application for all clients. They *must* use their professional judgement and personal knowledge of the client.

CHANGES IN SKIN RESISTANCE

As an example of how important this treatment responsibility is and must rest with the therapist, it is only necessary to consider how a skin will change over a course of treatment, and over a period will alter in the resistance it presents to the galvanic current. For example, a very blocked seborrhoeic skin will commence the treatment programme offering considerable resistance to the galvanic current, being compacted in nature, greasy on the surface, blocked within the follicle with oily matter (sebum), skin debris, etc., which has oxidized with air contact, and become slightly keratinized, horny and solid in nature like a plug. This surface film presents an effective barrier level which the galvanic current has to overcome. It is like a barrier to the electrical current in several ways: it is *dry* in nature, not liquid and moist which the current prefers; it is *oily,* always an effective barrier to electrical current transmission; and it is a *thick compacted layer,* hence physically thicker for the galvanic current to pass through. So initial treatments will take longer to overcome the resistance the skin presents, and application will take longer to get an effect and a higher level of skin resistance will register on the meter in milliamps, before the client tells of experiencing a sensation on the skin, or getting a metallic taste in the mouth.

As the programme of treatment progresses, measures will be employed to clear the skin of surface oils, free the blockages (galvanic desincrustation being the most effective measure itself), and refine the skin, thus changing its compacted condition, by peeling, deep-cleansing measures, steaming, ozone vapour, masks and normalizing processes (galvanic ionization being again one of the most effective means available). By these professional routines, strongly reinforced by a corrective programme of home cleansing, and normalizing using the ampoules for deep-cleansing and seborrhoea, the skin will show a steady and persistent improvement in texture, colour, and general appearance. It will also become thinner, more hydrated, show a finer appearance and become more liable to sensitivity, reactions, etc. Being less dry, compacted, oily and blocked, it will present less of a barrier to the galvanic current. So skin reactions and client awareness will occur at a much earlier stage with a much lower reading on the meter registering the skin resistance in milliamps.

In fact, this change in the skin resistance reading on the meter can be used as a guide to skin improvement and progress. It provides an effective means of determining the skin's sensitivity, and provides additional guidance to the therapist as to changes in the skin condition, and overall differences in the skin diagnosis or analysis.

A dehydrated skin will also register a change as its condition becomes more hydrated and in better skin health, but the change will not be so dramatic. However, both instances serve to show how it must be the skin at that time, its sensitivity, overall reaction, and the client's response to the sensation which determine the application of galvanic treatment, length of application and level of intensity or degree of skin resistance. From this information also comes the knowledge to plan the treatment programme, durations between appointments, home care sequences, etc., frequency of ampoule use at home, etc.

5

Skin conditions

SKIN DIAGNOSIS/ANALYSIS

On their own, or in combined programmes of treatment, galvanic applications bring about visible changes in the skin, and they are well known for providing effective results. For the blocked skin particularly, the deep dissolving, cleansing effect on the horny plugs of blackheads has made the practice of manual extraction (pressing out of the contents of the blocked pores) totally unnecessary. It was always harmful to the skin, and quite futile, causing deep scarring to the basal layer of the skin, which reflected on the skin's surface in indentations and pock marks, lumpy texture, etc. It was, however, always very popular with the beauty industry who felt it answered the client's blocked skin problems, which of course it did not, as the enlarged pores simply reblocked, as the root cause had not been dealt with. Now by attacking the problem from both sides, unblocking, and normalizing the secretions at the same time, great results can be obtained, though of course the skin will always stay rather oily, that being its natural state dictated from within the body through hormone influence. It will no longer be blocked or blemished however, and its over-secretion can be controlled and gradually brought back into normal balance.

Changes such as these are possible only if the correct choice of application is made, based on accurate diagnosis of the skin and its needs. Applying the galvanic treatment is a simple procedure, but deciding how to go about obtaining results can be much more difficult.

If some basic points of skin diagnosis are considered, it may be easier to work out where the advantages of galvanic treatment can be used to the greatest effect.

If the skin is blocked or compacted and does not shed easily, it can be encouraged to do so by the desincrustation procedure, which is *always accomplished on a negative charge,* with the machine switched to negative (−). This is mainly used on the younger skins, but can be used periodically to deep cleanse and free older skins, and make the surface more receptive to the more effective hydrating, regenerating elements of the ionization or penetration aspects of galvanic treatment (iontophoresis). Only if the mature skin is excessively dehydrated or very taut should this procedure not be used, as it is a deep-cleansing but also drying procedure, and could cause skin irritation. Then another means of deep-cleansing could be used, such as vapourzone (ozone steaming) and vacuum suction (lymphatic drainage).

So as a deep-cleansing, unblocking, freeing, and desincrustation and preparation measure, the desincrustation procedure is invaluable for any skins that need and can take the effects of the application. The intensity, duration, and frequency of the application can be altered according to the skin and its needs. A young skin may benefit from twice weekly applications, while a skin in its middle twenties to early thirties may only need deep-cleansing once a month.

If the skin requires hydration, regeneration, biological stimulation, or has a specific problem such as seborrhoea, pigmentation, or sensitivity (dilated capillaries, etc.), this can be accomplished using the iontophoresis method of penetration or ionization of active substances into the skin on a galvanic charge. The electrically charged ions in the ampoules vary as to polarity and some will penetrate on a positive, some on a negative charge. These active ions are termed cations and anions. There are a few ampoules which contain both cations and anions within them, that is positively charged and negatively charged elements. These ampoules require the use of both polarities for full penetration of all the active ingredients, normally applied first negatively, then after returning the polarity changer through zero, applied positively. First some of the active elements flow across the link the galvanic current and water provides, then the rest follow as the polarity of the indifferent electrode is altered on the machine to attract them.

Therapists have only to follow polarity instructions as given by the manufacturers, or must base their judgement on the pH of the ingredients, that is the acidity or alkalinity of the substance.

SKIN NEEDS/HOME CARE

Therapists will be able to assess the skin's need for ionization of active preparations by *visual inspection* of the skin, by *touch* to assess texture, skin elasticity, sensitivity, and by very thorough *verbal discussion* of the skin behaviour history, allergic reactions, etc., with the client. The client's age, health, medications used, home skin care routines, etc., all bear a relationship to the effect of the galvanic iontophoresis and the benefit that could be gained.

As it is a very effective, and therefore active routine, it is important to check the home treatment the skin is getting, and ideally to have the same range of supporting and complementary preparations used at home to reinforce the effect achieved. In many cases it is not only desirable but essential to ensure success, and the value of this can be easily explained to the client who relies on the therapist's professional judgement.

'GALLERY LINE'

To ensure success, use and advise a complimentary treatment range such as Gallery Line, *formulated to provide effective results*

In any event it is necessary to check that the client is not using any preparations within home care which in combination with clinic applications could cause an adverse or bad reaction within the skin. For example, if a client is having collagen ampoules applied within her professional treatment, then only the same range of collagen ampoules, or complementary collagen creams, etc., should be used for home reinforcement, advised by the therapist. Otherwise an irritant reaction could occur as a result of the combined effect being overactive and causing skin sensitivity. The manufacturers of treatment preparations have now made it so easy for therapists to devise clinic and home care routines that work well together without over-reactions, that a combined programme based on one range of items should be advised wherever possible. The manufacturer is expert at his job, the therapist excellent at hers, and by working together they can achieve spectacular results for the client, which luckily the therapist gets all the credit for.

CLIENT'S RECORD CARD

FACIAL TREATMENT CARD   Name:

Address:		Tel: Work	Home
Medical history:	Medication		

SKIN ASSESSMENT   Date   Date   Date

Seborrhoea				Open pores				Blocked pores			
Blackheads				Acne				Scars			
Delicate				Dry				Dehydrated			
Mature				Atrophic (ageing)				Loss of firmness			
Sun-tan				Dilated capillaries				Pigmentation			
Superfluous hair				Skin tags				Moles			

TREATMENT PLAN	Products/ampoules	Advised for home use	Purchased
Date 1			
2			
3			
4			
5			
6			

Reassess the skin carefully after six treatments to judge changes in skin condition, success of home product use and make changes in clinic and home routines as required.

PROGRESS COMMENT:

Treatment Plan	Products/ampoules	Advised for home use	Purchased
7			
8			
9			
10			
11			
12			
REPEAT ASSESSMENT			
13			
14			
15			
16			
17			
18			

Home Care Check List

SKIN CARE	Following professional products advised	Using different range at home	Regular home use		Irratic home use
AMPOULES	Used weekly	Twice weekly	Three times weekly		Daily
MASKS	Used weekly	Twice weekly	Three times weekly		

Beauty Education International — Brindley Road South, Exhall, Coventry. Telephone: (0203) 362505.

SKIN CONDITIONS AIDED BY AMPOULE THERAPY AND GALVANISM

Overactivity of the skin	— Seborrhoea — Enlarged pores — Over-secretion of oil	Desincrustation and normalizing. Ampoules to correct over-functioning and improve hydric balance, based on herbal, plant, marine and vitamin extracts.
Under-functioning of the skin	— Dehydration — Ageing tendencies — Poor biological function	Ampoules for hydration, normalizing skin balance, regenerating, etc., based on placenta, collagen, embryonic extracts, vitamins and plants.
Hypersensitivity	— Tendency to irritation — Dilated capillaries — Skin reddening	Ampoules based on soothing and skin calming aspects, also designed to strengthen capillaries, based on camomile, azulen, and aloe vera.

OVERACTIVE SKIN CONDITIONS

Acne, blocked seborrhoeic skin with inclination to impurities, enlarged pores, surface oil and comedones (blackheads) are all signs of over-functioning of the skin.

AMPOULE TREATMENT — DESINCRUSTATION
(DEEP-CLEANSING AND UNBLOCKING)

This treatment is the intensive deep-cleansing of the skin with the desincrustation process, sometimes referred to as lysing, using ampoules containing a mixture of natural substances designed to dissolve the oily blockage. These start to free the surface sebum or natural oil of the skin which with the associated dead skin cells, perspiration salts, etc., form the hair follicle plugs or blackheads which cause enlarged pores and the infected follicles of acne vulgaris.

This loosening, decomposing, freeing action naturally and gently releases the skin blockage over a period of time, clearing the skin without causing it damage. The process also makes the skin more receptive to the corrective or normalizing treatments. These include ionization using special ampoules to balance the oil flow and prevent reformation of the blocked pores.

AMPOULE TREATMENT — IONTOPHORESIS FOR CORRECTING OR NORMALIZING SEBORRHOEA

This is a specific treatment for oily, seborrhoeic, troubled skins with a tendency to impurities, pustules and associated scarring. Ampoules for seborrhoea include a variety of active ingredients depending on supplier. These could include chlorophyll, camomile extracts (for calming and healing), vitamins B1, B2, B6, and vitamin E (regenerative effects), astringent plant extracts, hamamelis (witch hazel), marine extracts, active herbs, and herbal elements.

These ampoules help to balance the skin secretions, bring the skin back into better functioning and health, appear to calm the skin, aid healing, and over a period reduce the over-secretion of the oil output. These ampoules remain in the skin to be effective and do their work, and they leave the skin feeling and looking very matt and pleasant. The active ingredients are formulated to be very compatible to this often rather over-treated and abused skin condition, and appear to calm and settle it very effectively, reducing the red colour in the skin. Seborrhoea ampoules are often used as a protective measure to the troubled skin, being applied by the client first thing in the morning after cleansing. These corrective ampoules, in combination with desincrustation, are an essential element in the successful treatment and control of the seborrhoeic, blemished or acne condition. With a combined programme of professional treatment and home care routines, using both desincrustation and corrective iontophoresis ampoules, results are excellent. The client is guided to use the cleansing and corrective ampoules regularly at home, naturally without galvanism, and this supports the effect achieved, and reinforces the progress and control of the problem. Establishing the correct home care measures is vital for success on this difficult skin.

PRODUCTS FOR CLINIC AND HOME USE

Active ampoules and Aqua *products for clinic and home use*

ENLARGED PORES

Different ampoules can be used to treat a skin with enlarged pores, sometimes as a progression of the seborrhoea condition as it comes under control, or where the skin is simply rather open textured or has enlarged pores from some other cause. Enlarged pores are normally associated with oily skin as it becomes less blocked and begins to refine, so its active ingredients are based on tightening elements including extracts of tannin, hamamelis (witch hazel) and oak bark. Herbal elements are also used to refine the skin naturally.

Other causes of enlarged pores are poor health, ineffective cleansing measures, loss of elasticity due to incorrect care or illness, or too fierce a treatment programme causing the skin to look over-strained and exposed with evident pores. Use of over-rich nourishing creams in a young skin can also cause the condition, but in all these cases the skin will not have associated excessive oil secretion, and must be treated with more gentle elements. Here the plant extracts and herbal-based ampoules are ideal as they refine slowly without too much drying action on the skin. So it is important to diagnose the skin correctly to get the correct effect and not obtain too active and unwanted a reaction.

The severity of the problem decides how often the treatment must be applied, and whether the ampoule products should be applied within the home care programme by the client. If the skin shows signs of sensitivity, the timing between applications can be extended. Normally the ampoule for enlarged pores has a very calming effect on the skin, while at the same time making it matt in appearance.

Ampoule therapy for the seborrhoeic and enlarged pore conditions may be positively or negatively charged according to the ingredients and the manufacturer's instructions. This depends not only on the actively charged ions in the solution but also on the acidity or alkalinity of the contents, remembering that acidic solutions (pH below 7) are used on a positive (+) charge, and alkaline solutions (pH above 7) are used on a negative (−) charge. The manufacturer's instructions should be followed as to polarity, but their advice as to skin resistance levels, length of application, etc., must only be used as guidance. The skin and the client sensitivity always act as the main source of guidance.

UNDER-FUNCTIONING OF THE SKIN

Dehydrated, dry, lifeless skin conditions, atrophy, ageing, loss of elasticity and skin tone, fine lines, softness and crepey skin texture, are all indications of skin under-functioning and can be

treated with ampoule therapy. The ampoules may also be applied as a preventative measure to avoid the conditions occurring prematurely.

AMPOULE TREATMENT — IONTOPHORESIS FOR STIMULATION, IMPROVED SKIN FUNCTIONING, ETC., 'DEHYDRATION'

Dry, lifeless, dehydrated, rough or chapped skin, or any condition requiring additional moisture such as associated with low-fat diets, illness, neglect, or sun-tanning can be treated with ampoule therapy. It is also useful for clients living in high altitude climates lacking natural moisture in the atmosphere and is an excellent preventative measure for the 20 to 30 age range to avoid dehydration and premature ageing. A useful first ampoule to use on any under-functioning skin is 'Dehydration' (moisturizing) to find out its reaction to the active effects of ampoule therapy or where more active effects are needed such as regeneration.

The ampoule therapy to use is 'Dehydration' (moisturizing), based on natural moisturizing factors (NMF), water-absorbent plant germ extracts, plant gels, and vitamin B2 (lactoflavin). The stabilized juice of the aloe vera plant is another valuable source of hydrating and moisturizing elements for ionization, also widely recognized for its soothing and stabilizing effects on skin tissue. Ginseng and wheatgerm extract also have excellent effects.

The moisturizing ampoule acts as an instant pick-up to tired, dehydrated skin, and quickly rectifies skin chapping, roughness, or peeling from careless skin care, over-exposure to sun, etc. The skin shows immediate improvement after the application, making the surface more smooth and supple, reducing tightness in the skin.

Used as a preventative measure against ageing tendencies it is an essential part of the treatment programme for the skin inclined to dryness, and helps prevent the formation of fine lines around the eyes, mouth, and on the neck. It is also useful to delay the fine crepey condition seen on necks even on quite young women, when the neck is neglected in the home care programme.

The ampoule remains in the skin after ionization, and is not rinsed off. Normal moisturizer can be applied after ampoule application, or a sun filter applied to provide skin protection if the client is living in a sunny climate, to prevent any additional loss of natural moisture.

Application may be negative or positive polarity according to ingredients and their ion activity. Follow the manufacturer's polarity instructions, but make your own decisions regarding the length of application, skin resistance, etc., based on skin reaction, erythema response, client sensation, etc.

Some moisture revitalizing ampoules may require both negative and positive polarity to allow all the active elements/ions to pass into the skin. First the negative polarity is applied, then the control returned to zero, and the polarity altered to positive, and this is then applied.

PRODUCTS FOR DRY SKIN

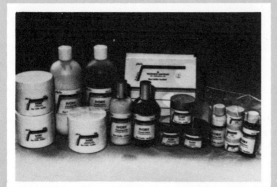

(a)

(a), (b) Dry and dehydrated skin needs special care such as the Ivory *range from* Gallery Line *for clinic and home treatment*

(b)

Always use a lower level of skin resistance (meter reading) and shorter duration of treatment when working with the positive pole because of its tightening effects on the skin. It is capable of causing irritant skin reactions so use with caution initially.

MATURE OR NEGLECTED SKIN — VISIBLE SIGNS OF AGEING

Physiological signs of ageing such as the under-functioning of cellular exchange and biological activity, signs of loss of elasticity, changes in skin tone, vigour, firmness of subcutaneous tissues, fine lines and an inclination to dryness and tightness in the skin's surface are signs of mature or neglected skin. The condition may be associated with a loss of firmness in the facial contours and points to combining the ampoule therapy with a routine incorporating facial muscle contraction to tone up underlying supportive muscles. This then acts to stimulate the skin from within, and from the surface, by natural stimulation through the action on the muscles and thereby on the circulation, and externally by activating measures' ampoule therapy for firming and stimulating the skin.

The ampoule therapy to use is 'Collagen', 'Elastin', or 'Placenta', for revitalizing, toning, and moisturizing effects. Active ingredients are based on organic substances from embryonic tissues, these being very effective for improving biological function in the skin tissues, so firming, tightening and regenerating in effect. The ampoules may also contain natural soluble collagen, cell-building substances extracted from protein. Vitamins A and B may also be used to delay signs of ageing in the skin tissue. These cell extracts in combination with germ extracts from plants, bring about a visible regeneration effect on the skin, making it firmer, smoother, more supple and elastic, and making the skin seem hydrated, puffed out, making fine wrinkle lines less noticeable.

MATURE, DELICATE SKIN

Mature, delicate skin needs active but also gentle regenerative actions to delay signs of ageing, formation of fine lines, skin imperfections, pigmentations, fibrous growths, etc. The mature or delicate skin has more tendency to sensitivity, and reaction. In some cases it is sensible to start ampoule therapy on this type of skin using a less active ampoule initially, such as one for hydration and moisturizing.

The ampoule therapy to use is 'Bio-Regenerator'; it consists of active ingredients including germ extracts from plants, vitamin A and E, and sometimes B vitamins. The effect of the regenerative

PRODUCTS FOR MATURE
SKIN

(a)

(a), (b) Mature skin needs active but gentle products such as the Amber Collagen *range from* Gallery Line *for clinic and home treatment*

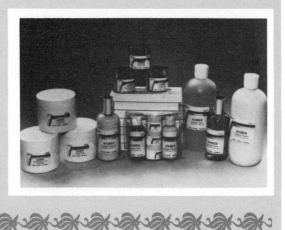

ampoule is to improve the skin's capacity to retain moisture, while improving its biological function. So it is highly effective as a preventative measure against the effects of ageing. It makes the skin more supple, improves its tone, firmness and most of all its vitality.

ATROPHY, MATURE SKIN, SCARRED SKIN OR NEGLECTED/ABUSED SKIN

Ampoule therapy can be applied on any demanding skin condition needing growth stimulation, such as compacted mature skin, old scarring from acne (when the condition is completely resolved), after illness or exposure to severe weather or high altitude, or simply atrophic and ageing skin where it has tremendous results in improving skin colour and vitality.

The ampoule therapy to use in this case is either 'Embryo', 'Placenta', 'Kolloid', 'Collagen', 'Elastin' or 'Royale Jelly', depending on the manufacturer, but all are based on very active elements. Ingredients in these ampoules are extremely complex and surprisingly, considering their active nature, seldom cause adverse reaction in the skin, seeming to be very complementary to its structure, being of natural origin. Ingredients include embryonic gels, vitamins A and E, lanolin, Royale Jelly (from bees' secretions), plant extracts, etc. In addition to these 'bio-stimulants' some embryonic ampoules contain vital amino acids, proteins, and fats and oils especially compatible with the skin. The ampoules contain a high proportion of growth stimulants and vitamins and are specifically used to help cellular growth, rebuild skin, and slow down ageing tendencies. They help reverse the process where the skin slows down its rate of *proliferation* (natural shedding) based on growth from the skin's basal layers, becoming compacted, poorly textured and coarse. They help the skin regain its youthful activity in a natural way, regenerating from within, to push the old dead skin's cells off from the surface.

In the case of atrophy and ageing skin, the problem is one of insufficient regeneration, inadequate nourishment of the skin and subcutaneous cells, and loss of natural oils and hydric (fluid) balance. Therefore a natural approach is needed to strengthen, regenerate and stimulate the skin over a course of treatment.

The embryonic or placenta ampoules result in a stimulation of the basal circulation, improving functioning of the dermal and epidermal cells, supported by the growth stimulation aspects of the preparation. The tissue concentrates, bio-stimulants, vitamins, etc., all play an important part in the regeneration, cell building process, and the skin quickly responds to the applications achieving a better texture, colour, elasticity, and smoothness.

If the skin is very compacted, then embryo/placenta ampoules may be combined in treatment with biological peeling, if the skin sensitivity permits, to speed the skin shedding and cellular rebuilding process.

In all cases of under-functioning of the skin, regular use of the treatment ampoules plus supportive creams, moisture preparations, etc., is vital for success. If home application of ampoules is advised, the client must be guided as to their use, how often they should be applied, etc. It may be necessary sometimes to advise the client to apply the ampoules in a concentrated manner, daily or three times a week, depending on the skin's need. Once a week is the normal application for home use. The method of application for iontophoresis for the mature, atrophied skin varies once again according to the active ingredients, and may be on a positive charge, a negative charge, or occasionally requiring both polarities, one after the other, with the application time divided between the polarities. The negative charge will always be applied first, being the penetrating pole, followed by the positive charge — for a very short period at low intensity. If in doubt about the skin's sensitivity to galvanism, apply only the negative pole at first and then work up to using both polarities.

HYPERSENSITIVITY, DILATED CAPILLARIES (COUPEROSE)

The condition of hypersensitivity normally relates to a physically thin skin, easily stimulated, prone to skin irritation and susceptible to surface damage resulting in dilated capillaries, also known as *couperose*.

This growing problem of hypersensitivity and tendency to reddening and irritation of the skin, is considered to be associated with the growing physiological and psychological stresses of modern day life. The pace at which life is led, the pressures and worries to which a person is exposed, all seem to take their toll on the individual in terms of increased susceptibility to nervous rashes, skin irritations, etc. Individual capacity to cope with and fight these nervous influences seems also to be decreasing, as people get more and more tense about life.

So the therapist will find an increasing need to treat these sensitivity problems, and needs gentle but effective products to aid her in her task. For a client who suffers from high colour, and who reacts badly to any stimulatory effect, such as drinking spirits, eating highly-seasoned foods, or being in a very hot or cold temperature, these ampoule products will be a welcome relief.

The ampoule therapy to use will be marked *Camomile* or *Aloe Vera* for 'Hypersensitivity' or 'Couperose', and is based on soothing ingredients such as camomile/azulen, aloe vera, plant substances known to have a constricting effect on tiny capillary vessels such as neroli (from orange blossom), and lavender. Sandalwood is another well known essential oil which is recognized as having calming effects on the skin, and the body's system. The ampoule may combine one or two of these essential elements to calm and balance the skin, or be based entirely on one element such as camomile or Aloe Vera (both used without galvanism in this case) which have a normalizing effect. The products for couperose also have an effect of tightening and constricting the surface blood vessels, and through gentle stimulation encourage the removal of trapped or stagnant blood away from the problem areas.

Choice of ampoule for either the sensitive or dilated capillary/couperose condition should be made carefully to avoid over-reaction, and if in doubt commence with the ampoule for hypersensitivity and progress to that for the dilated blood vessel condition. The ampoules are extremely effective for improving the dilation problem, as they appear to strengthen the capillaries' walls, and improve their elasticity, preventing further breakdown of the vascular structure in the area. Naturally the effect is only retained by regular application of the ampoule, supported by good home care based on the same elements, for it is only a control measure: nothing can mend the skin fragility in the area, or make it less susceptible to damage. Preventing the cause of the damage is the most important element in the treatment of the sensitive or couperose condition, so a close look at the client's skin care habits, sun-tanning protection, etc., is essential.

Some ampoules for hypersensitivity and couperose are not intended for ionization, and this will be clearly indicated on the box and with the

manufacturer's instructions. This means they have been formulated to obtain their effect by applying them manually. Some ampoules, such as Aloe Vera, can be used with or without galvanic current depending on the skin condition they are used for. In the case of the sensitive skin, just use these ampoules manually.

PRODUCTS FOR SENSITIVE
SKIN

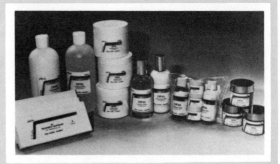

(a)

(a), (b) Sensitive skin needs a special approach in treatment such as Opal *products from* Gallery Line *for clinic and home use*

(b)

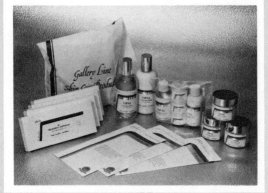

SPECIAL CONDITIONS
— PIGMENTATION PROBLEMS

Pigmentation problems include pigmentation patches, hyper-pigmentation (increased colour) and pigmentation associated with pregnancy or use of the contraceptive pill.

Ampoule therapy will be for 'Pigmentation' and will work to reduce the problem; it will brighten the skin, bleach the colour of senile pigmentation (often referred to as kidney spots or freckles), and reduce the intensity of areas of deep skin colour associated with pregnancy or the Pill. The ampoule is based on a concentrated solution of ascorbic acid (pure vitamin C) together with an alcoholic solution of plant extracts designed to reduce pigmentation. This produces a bleaching effect, or a reduction in the intensity of the skin discolouration and also helps prevent the reoccurrence of the problem or delays new pigmentation.

The ampoule treatment is used in combination with desincrustation, biological peeling, compresses or vapourzone applications, depending on skin texture and sensitivity. After treatment the skin must be protected by sun protection moisturizers, or sun blockers, and the client asked to avoid sun exposure. Pigmentation ampoule therapy is applied entirely within the professional situation by a qualified therapist trained in the special techniques involved. The treatment itself is not difficult to apply, but knowledge of when not to apply the pigmentation procedure requires experience, so if in any doubt therapists should not attempt the treatment. Ampoules for pigmentation should not be applied close to, during, or immediately following the monthly menstruation, as the body's natural hormone levels will be high at this time. This minimizes the effect that can be expected, so treatment should be suspended for a few days around this time of the month.

The client does not participate in any actual ampoule application at home, but rather is advised on protective measures to avoid a reoccurrence of the condition. Pigmentation treatment is a highly active and effective routine to which the client may well have a reaction. It is always best to know the skin and its reactions before giving the pigmentation treatment to be on the safe side and avoid unwanted side-effects. Therapists should supervise the treatment and its after-effects closely, and be prepared to adapt or change the course of the treatment plan if necessary. The application may vary according to the manufacturer, and therapists must follow the polarity directions given, once more using their own judgement as to skin resistance and duration of the application. How often the ampoule should be applied also depends on the reactions obtained.

Results will depend on the client's ability to change her lifestyle if the problem is sun-linked, or if connected with senile pigmentation then the results will only provide a control, not a cure. If the client is young, results can be excellent, especially if the problems are helped by a reduction in the body's natural hormone balance, either by the natural drop in hormones experienced following childbirth, or by changing to a lower hormone dosage Pill for contraceptive purposes. It cannot be expected that the client will change her family planning methods just for the sake of a pigmentation problem, but she can alter its form with medical guidance if the condition causes her distress.

BEAUTY GALLERY IN USE

(a)

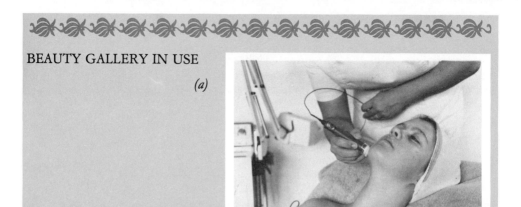

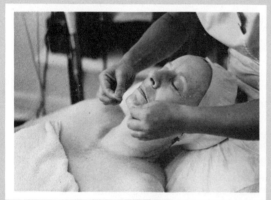

(b) Combined treatments to achieve results

(c) Interlinking galvanism with complementary related facial application

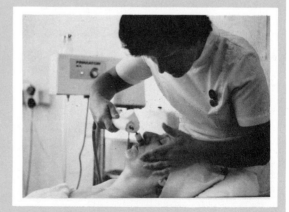

COMBINED TREATMENT SUGGESTIONS USING GALVANISM

DEEP-CLEANSING ROUTINES — ½ HOUR AND 1 HOUR TREATMENTS

1 hour treatment for seborrhoeic, thickened skin
Cleanse, biological peel with vapour steam, desincrustation (−), vacuum (lymphatic drainage), desquamating mask (fuller's earth or sulphur-based). Iontophoresis using seborrhoea ampoule (i.e. active herbs).

½ hour treatment for deep-cleansing
Desincrustation (on skin with no make-up). Vacuum suction under vapour and ozone (no oil medium used, suction operates on steam alone). Iontophoresis for correction using ampoule for seborrhoea or open pores, depending on the degree of the problem.

½ hour treatment for deep-cleansing (alternative method)
Cleanse, desincrustation, cleansing desquamating mask, direct high-frequency treatment or iontophoresis for seborrhoea or enlarged pores.

MOISTURIZING AND REGENERATING ROUTINES — 1 HOUR TREATMENTS

1 hour treatment for stimulation, hydration, biological function
Cleansing, plus specialized cleansing with peeling-type product, or short duration biological peeling under vapour if the skin is suitable, or desincrustation to prepare the skin for massage with regenerating creams, oils, or hydrating elements according to type.
Biological or lifting mask.
Iontophoresis of active ampoules for moisturizing, regeneration, or maintenance purposes. (Ampoules to be used include 'Dehydration', 'Placenta', 'Collagen', 'Embryo', 'Ginseng', 'Wheatgerm'.) Products left in the skin, plus moisture or sun protection if needed.

1 hour treatment for dry, dehydrated, lifeless skin	Basic cleansing or brush cleansing for skin stimulation. Iontophoresis for moisture, loss of elasticity, atrophy, ageing tendencies using ampoules for specific effects. Massage with oil or cream over the area of ampoule therapy. Remaining cream can be gently removed, and the skin settled with a vapourizer spray (no tonic used, simply pure or mineral water). Moisture protection.
1 hour treatment for dry, dehydrated, lifeless skin (alternative method)	Basic or brush cleansing, massage with indirect high-frequency treatment (Viennese massage), biological mask; iontophoresis concluding the treatment, for specific effect, left in the skin. Spray toning, no drying effects. Moisture protection.
Regenerative and stimulatory routines for atrophic and ageing skin	Basic cleanse and deep-cleansing with vapour and suction (lymphatic drainage). Active biological mask to increase the skin regeneration rate. Muscle contraction with the facial applicator, or full face mask or jaw strap (interferential method). Iontophoresis for delaying ageing tendencies, and to increase skin elasticity. Ampoules to be used are 'Placenta', 'Embryo', 'Collagen & Elastin', 'Bio-Regenerator', with the product left in the skin and used as a matt base for moisture or sun protection if needed.
Regenerative routine (alternative method)	Brush cleanse. Facial and shoulder massage — 20 minutes' duration Biological or lifting mask. Iontophoresis for specific effect, using regenerating, hydrating and stimulating effects. Moisture or sun protection.

HOME CARE SUPPORT FOR TREATMENT PROGRAMMES

All the ampoules used within professional therapy (apart from the pigmentation ampoules) can be used without galvanism at home by the client. This will reinforce the effects of the clinic application, though naturally the action is not as effective when the ampoules are used in this way.

CLIENT'S AMPOULE BROCHURE

Impressive literature builds home sales, and saves the therapist a lot of precious time

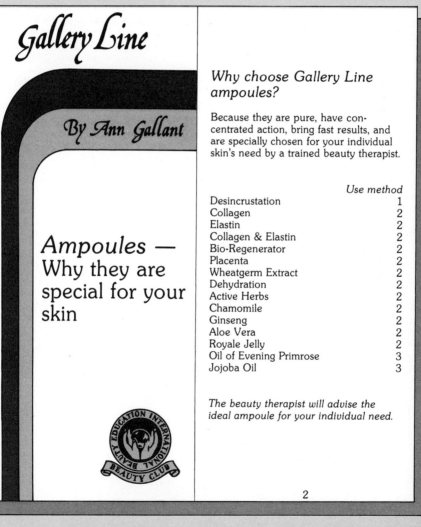

Gallery Line

By Ann Gallant

Ampoules — Why they are special for your skin

Why choose Gallery Line ampoules?

Because they are pure, have con-centrated action, bring fast results, and are specially chosen for your individual skin's need by a trained beauty therapist.

	Use method
Desincrustation	1
Collagen	2
Elastin	2
Collagen & Elastin	2
Bio-Regenerator	2
Placenta	2
Wheatgerm Extract	2
Dehydration	2
Active Herbs	2
Chamomile	2
Ginseng	2
Aloe Vera	2
Royale Jelly	2
Oil of Evening Primrose	3
Jojoba Oil	3

The beauty therapist will advise the ideal ampoule for your individual need.

2

The use of ampoules in home advised programmes involves the client in her own progress and ensures fast results. This is especially important when the client is not able to visit the clinic as often as would be liked or as would be needed to obtain the desired results for her. Whether through circumstances or finances, where visits are rather spaced, such as with the young client with slender finances, then she can be encouraged to do a lot for herself at home. At least the clinic knows that she is following the correct plan, and is purchasing her treatment requirements from the best source to ensure success.

Why Ampoules are Special for Your Skin

The sealed ampoule provides the ideal means of presenting the delicate and complex substances needed for skin improvement and ensures the active elements remain fresh and pure until applied.

Ampoule therapy — both in the clinic and at home — provides a direct and concentrated treatment for skin improvement and maintenance. Designed to bring fast results, ampoules form an essential part of the *Gallery Line Skin Care* range by Ann Gallant, with each individual home plan worked out by a trained beauty therapist.

The precious contents of the ampoules can be made to penetrate deeply into the skin in the clinic using galvanic iontophoresis, or applied manually with gentle massage at home according to the therapist's advice. The ampoules must be stored in a cool place, out of direct sunlight, and opened immediately prior to application for full effect. They are opened with a sharp snap of the narrow end with fingers protected by a tissue.

Application may be daily, twice weekly, or weekly, according to the skin's need, and the beauty therapist will advise the exact routine for your skin's special requirements. Ampoules are for external use only, and the best way to use them at home is to open them directly into your hand and apply immediately on to the skin.

3

How to use at home

Method 1 — Apply on wet skin, massage in thoroughly for a few minutes and then rinse off to achieve a deep cleansing action.

Method 2 — Apply *either* to give a finishing touch to your morning routine of skin care, instead of or before moisture protection, *or* apply at night, instead of or before night skin nourishment.

Method 3 — Apply at night instead of night cream, and may be applied all over the face and body.

4

When actual changes in the skin condition are required, then regular application of the active ampoules is vital. Ideally this should be accomplished within the clinic, but if this is not the case, then the next best method is to explain the necessary home routines and daily care to the client, and show her how to incorporate the application of the chosen ampoule into her routine regularly at specific intervals. Normally this is weekly, but in cases of difficult skin, where an improvement is wanted quickly, then the application can be twice or three times weekly, or in severe cases even daily. It depends how much the client wants the improvement, and needs it, and this partly determines the effect

Desincrustation   1

A deep skin cleansing formula for correction of oily, large pored, blocked or blemished skin. Naturally dissolves the oil blockage and allows corrective treatment to be effective in normalizing the skin. May need to be a daily treatment until the skin secretion becomes regulated and skin condition and texture is regained.

Collagen   2

A skin conditioning formula to improve skin tone, texture and moisture, through increased biological function in the skin. Ideal for the younger woman with a dehydrated or neglected skin, or to preserve a youthful complexion and delay signs of ageing. In the mature skin, works to improve skin elasticity, surface moisture and delay fine lines and loss of texture.

Elastin   2

Improves elasticity in the skin and is particularly effective on the younger skin showing premature lines, loss of texture, and poor skin tone. Within a programme of treatment, stimulates the skin, improving function, and restoring the correct oil and moisture balance.

Collagen and Elastin   2

A formula designed to help the mature skin with a loss of both texture and tone, and showing visible signs of ageing, lines, skin frailty, crepiness on the neck, and around the eyes. Contains elements the skin is able to accept without irritation, and provides excellent results in treatment and at home. Stimulates the skin to improved functioning and provides skin tightening effects without drying or irritating the surface. Should be used within a compatible skin care programme such as the *Amber Collagen Range*.

Bio-Regenerator   2

An essential treatment after suntanning, exposure to extremes of temperature, or for overstrained skins which have suffered severe dehydration from neglect, poor health, or over stringent dieting. Premature ageing and loss of texture in the younger person from sun-bed tanning also responds to the Bio-Regenerator formula. It works to stimulate cellular replacement in the skin's deeper layers, so is also useful in cases of scarring or where pigmentation patches are a problem. May be used on all but the most sensitive skins within a supporting home care programme.

5

6

and expense she will give to the home care supportive measures advised. The therapist has only to advise what is correct for the skin, and what is the best method to achieve results without over-treatment or side-effects. If the skin needs a lot of home correction, this should be advised in a positive way to impress upon the client the importance of this aspect and how it relates to overall results. For it is an actual fact that without home care support, the results will be very difficult, if not impossible, to obtain.

The client may need to use the ampoules in an intensive fashion over a 10 or 14 day period to gain a progressive improvement,

---

Placenta   2

A regenerating formula for the mature and dehydrated skin, providing gentle stimulation from within the skin, without irritation to the surface capillaries. Improves skin function, oil and moisture balance, and tone, making this a most useful ampoule for the more sensitive mature skin. Also very beneficial to the younger person as a maintenance measure, to preserve a good complexion and delay ageing tendencies.

Wheatgerm Extract   2

A soothing and nourishing formula for the dry skin with a tendency to capillary weakness, which revitalizes the skin without irritation. Ideal as a calming and controlling measure on the mature easily stimulated skin with high colour. The wheatgerm extract is in a spirit base, making this an ideal treatment for the dry but not sensitive skin. If extreme sensitivity is present the ampoules Chamomile or Aloe Vera are more beneficial.

Dehydration   2

A moisture concentrate which brings immediate relief to the dry, tight or chapped skin. Containing natural moisturizers which the skin can use immediately, the ampoule is the ideal one to commence ampoule therapy and gauge skin reaction before proceeding to more active ampoules if needed. Dehydration is the best ampoule for the younger person to maintain skin condition, and leaves the skin feeling smooth and supple. It replaces natural moisture lost through suntanning etc., and may be used on a wide range of skin conditions, including the oily young skin, to help rebuild skin texture after the corrective ampoules have done their work.

Active Herbs   2

An essential curative ampoule to regulate the oily and troubled skin, and bring it back to correct functioning. Regular use within a home programme will refine the skin, reduce irritation in the skin, and give a matt settled appearance to the surface. Used in conjunction with Desincrustation ampoules and the *Aqua Skin Care* range, Active Herbs will quickly improve the skin condition. Based on natural curative and soothing herbal elements, the ampoule provides a gentle means of improving this difficult skin condition.

7

8

such as in cases of extreme dehydration after illness or over-exposure to suntanning, or in a case of ageing, lined or slack skin. Where quick results are needed to help the client, then she should be advised how this help can be gained, and exactly what she must do herself to take a positive part in her own improvement. Clients are normally so thrilled and impressed with the results obtained with these ampoule applications that they do not begrudge the costs involved. If you have a blemished skin which can be cleared, no cost is too great to pay for the clear complexion. Likewise, for the mature skin showing its owner's age really clearly, any visible improvement will be cherished.

Camomile 2

A very special ampoule for calming the difficult and easily irritated skin, based on the extract of Camomile. Ideal for any skin suffering from sensitivity; it is mainly used on the delicate complexion, and provides excellent protection from external irritation. Leaves the skin smooth, supple and refreshed, while providing essential moisture in the skin.

Ginseng 2

A formula based on the renowned properties of Ginseng which can both stimulate and improve functioning in the tissues, leaving the skin smooth hydrated and glowing. An excellent maintenance and conditioning treatment for the dry, dehydrated and mature skin, which increases the skin's ability to resist capillary damage (couperose). It may also be used as part of the regeneration programme for the younger troubled skin, once the remedial programme is complete.

Aloe Vera 2

A formula which provides gentle regeneration of the skin, whilst having a calming and healing action. Aloe Vera is a plant extract in a form easily accepted by the skin and its main application will be on the younger dry or dehydrated skin. It is especially useful if the skin is rather sensitive to the more active ampoules or has areas of dilated capillaries which limit treatment. Aloe Vera has a very varied application because of its soothing effects in the skin, and can be used in combination with all the *Gallery Line Skin Care* ranges.

Royale Jelly 2

Based on bees' secretion. The Royale Jelly ampoule provides a unique stimulating and firming action on the skin without dryness or irritation. Complex natural elements improve biological function in the skin, causing cellular regeneration to improve skin texture, tone and smoothness. Extremely rich in active elements, the ampoule is easily absorbed and accepted by dry, dehydrated and mature skins, and provides spectacular results for the discerning woman who treasures her complexion.

9

10

GENERAL POINTS IN GALVANIC TREATMENT

The use of galvanism for introducing active substances into the skin, or for freeing the skin from unwanted surface debris and blockage, is a valuable tool to the therapist. It is perhaps the most useful new treatment to be introduced to the profession in recent years, as it can provide such a wide range of differing effects.

Oil of Evening Primrose 3

A very fine oil in a concentrated and pure form which leaves the skin in a silky, smooth condition. One ampoule will provide a complete treatment for the face and body, and for maximum effect it should be carefully smoothed into the skin after a warm bath or shower. It will be absorbed completely into the skin, and its extract of Oil of Evening Primrose will work to stimulate the dry, dehydrated or mature skin.

11

Jojoba Oil 3

A super fine nourishing oil which provides a very luxurious treatment for the face and body, and allows the skin to absorb the product completely to improve surface dryness, loss of moisture, etc. One of the most effective new oils available to nourish the skin; in ampoule form the product is pure and at its most active and beneficial for the dry, dehydrated or mature skin. May be used all over the face and body.

12

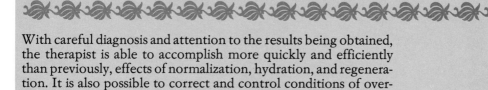

With careful diagnosis and attention to the results being obtained, the therapist is able to accomplish more quickly and efficiently than previously, effects of normalization, hydration, and regeneration. It is also possible to correct and control conditions of over-production of the skin's natural functions, seborrhoea and enlarged pores, and help the acne problem with medical liaison.

So for nearly all clients, galvanism has something valuable to contribute, if the therapist is skilled in its use.

6

Practical points

AMPOULES AND THEIR ACTIONS

A close look at galvanism — the way it works and its advantages in treatment — revealed its unique ability to cross the intact skin taking with it active elements directly into the skin's deeper layers, to provide immediate and visible improvements in the skin's appearance. It was seen that to gain full benefit the therapist had not only to understand the electrical frequency and its effects, but must also recognize her client's needs and match these against the actions of the ampoules.

Remember, galvanism provides the means to make the ampoules work, and in combination with carefully chosen products can provide spectacular results — *if the ampoule is matched accurately to the condition.* Ampoules can have *curative, regulatory, stimulatory,* or *calming effects.* So once a problem is assessed correctly, its remedy, through ampoule therapy, incorporated into treatment and backed by sound home care advice, is not far away.

AMPOULES

A wide range of ampoules are available to meet differing skin conditions

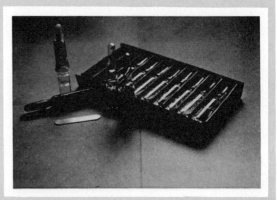

CHOOSING THE AMPOULE TO USE

An area that causes more uncertainty than any other is the actual choice of ampoule. This should not worry you at all, just think of ampoule therapy as beauty treatment in another effective form. The question is, what effect is needed to help the skin? Does it need *hydration, regeneration* (if lacking moisture or slowing down in its activity), *balancing and controlling* (overactivity of sebaceous glands, blockage, etc.), *stimulation* (to maintain texture, tone and prevent pigmentation problems), or *calming and strengthening* (if its capillary structure is weak and prone to sensitivity)?

Or, has the client a *special problem* of scars, pigmentation patches, over-vascularity, loss of skin tone from ill health, severe weight loss or incorrect choice of cosmetic skin care products? The skin may even have a special need for specialized 'bio-repair' regeneration ampoules if suntanning and heat exposure has been overdone.

The beauty operator has only to trust her knowledge of the skin, and working on from that, choose the right ampoule to do the job — starting with less effective ampoules and working up gradually once the skin's reactions to treatment are well known.

KNOWING WHAT TO USE — LOOK, FEEL, ASK THE QUESTIONS

How is it possible to know what to use just by looking at the skin? How do you gauge the skin's needs and what will be effective — moisture — collagen — royale jelly — active herbs — bio-repair, etc? How these decisions are made is very simple and all beauty operators working with the skin have the knowledge if they care to apply it.

It all relates to knowing the skin and the client, finding out about their age and health, their present diet, and seeing how this affects their skin moisture/oil levels, its tone and elasticity, sensitivity, and tendency to problems — pigmentation, blemishes, dilated capillary, frailty, etc. By looking at the skin, feeling it, and asking sensible questions of the client, it is possible to find out everything that you need to know to work out a really effective treatment plan.

Looking at the person as a whole tells you a lot about their skin, and the reasons for its present condition. It also points the direction for the remedy if the skin is not in good condition. There is no reason to make a client feel depressed about her skin, after all that is why she has come for help, for improvement, but honest advice to bring about fast improvement is necessary, and the therapist must be confident that she has the answers and can produce the results needed. Ampoule therapy will help provide these fast changes in the skin which give the client confidence, and make her feel in expert hands.

For example if a client is following a severe low fat diet, and is in her middle years, her skin will show evidence of this loss of fats, both in loss of supporting subcutaneous tissues — as stored fat is lost from beneath the skin, revealing contours — and in a softening of skin tone and texture as vital fats, so important to skin health, are reduced. (Essential nutrients, vitamins A and D and essential tissue-building factors are all present in fats.) Ampoule therapy plus good home care measures can help enormously to balance the ageing effects on the skin. Because this *total approach* is not always used in beauty therapy, clients often end up looking thinner and worse than before because they have loose skin, wrinkled baggy necks, crepey skin over the breasts, around the eyes, etc. It need not happen, but often the slimmer person looks older than before, facially. Ampoule therapy is one of the best things a therapist has to offer her clients when they are putting a

lot of strain on their skins, either through dieting, living a stressful life, suntanning, or when they have little time for cosmetic routines and want fast results.

No client minds paying if she gets the results she wants — ampoule therapy and its closely related home sales are a very professional and profitable way of providing these results.

AMPOULE ACTIONS
— CHOOSING FOR EFFECT

The first thing is to see what effect is needed, and match this against the known effects of the ampoules, which are based on a wide range of ingredients, mainly of natural, herbal and plant origin. Some contain animal extracts, while others contain soluble collagen. Unusual and highly effective action sources such as royal jelly, from bees' secretions, and ginseng, a root known to have very effective stimulatory yet calming properties, are also available. The therapist has a tremendous range at her fingertips, and can experiment once she has a good knowledge of the skin she is working with.

Ampoule therapy covers all treatments that use galvanic current to complete the treatment, plus ampoules which are individually packed in glass containers, but may not require galvanism to complete their application. Desincrustation and cellulite treatments — though not always in sealed individual ampoule form — should always be thought of as ampoule therapy, as they use galvanism to achieve their active effects. As desincrustation is soap-based and is washed from the skin after doing its dissolving of blockage work, it does not pass into the skin's deeper layers — it does not need to — its main benefit is to treat surface oil, seborrhoea and blackheads. Other corrective ampoules are used to balance the oil secretion — desincrustation helps remove it once formed and controls its presence.

KNOW YOUR PRODUCTS

One of the best ways to build knowledge about ampoules is to read manufacturers' literature, and look up the actions of the ingredients. Top professional product houses give excellent technical information brochures on their ranges, including ampoules, and the operator only has to match this against the skin's needs to gain a good result. Why one ampoule is preferred to another when both have similar actions and application will be mainly a thing of experience. Just as some skins respond better to one type of cream than another, so skins will be seen to 'come alive' more visibly when one ampoule is used than another. That is what makes ampoule therapy so interesting for the operator, she has to use her eyes and her brain to get the best results.

Gallery Line Ampoules

COLLAGEN (− −> +) CLINIC USE

The ampoule Collagen provides an excellent treatment for the younger dry skin, and helps combat the effects of sunbathing, over-stringent dieting, and the stresses and strain of modern living. It is also an ideal way to keep the skin in good condition and delay the formation of fine lines, or loss of elasticity and tone in the skin, associated with ageing. The Collagen ampoule acts on a biological function in the skin, and is most effective on the client aged between 25–35 years. It is used in association with the *Gallery Line Ivory Skin Care Range,* within clinic and home advised treatment, and a typical professional routine would be the classic *Facial Routine of 1 hour* including galvanic iontophoresis for penetrating the active product at the conclusion of the routine.

TREATMENT IN THE CLINIC — (USING GALLERY LINE PRODUCTS)

Cleanse the face and neck with *Ivory Cleansing Milk* using manual or brush methods. Remove the cleanser thoroughly with damp cotton wool, tissues or sponges. Spray tone the skin with a diluted solution of *Ivory Toning Lotion* using a vapourizer spray or tone manually using the product diluted on to a wet cotton-wool pad.

Massage the face and neck with *Ivory Night Cream* to which a small amount of Oil of Evening Primrose (in ampoule form) may be added if the skin is very dehydrated or has been neglected or put under strain. Massage for 10–15 minutes according to the client's needs, and then remove the product very thoroughly with damp cotton wool or tissues. The amount of cream/oil the skin absorbs will help guide on the home advised skin care plan.

If necessary, the skin may be spray toned again at this stage to ensure thorough removal of the product, once more using diluted *Ivory Toning Lotion.* A mask is then applied over the face and neck. The *Ivory Face Mask* or the *Opal Hydrating mask* (or both, on different areas of the face/neck) may be applied according to the action needed. The *Ivory Face Mask* is more stimulating while the *Opal Hydrating Mask* is more effective for dehydration problems. Leave the mask for 10 minutes to work, then remove carefully. Make sure the skin is really clean in preparation for galvanic iontophoresis. *Do not tone the skin at this stage. Apply galvanic iontophoresis with the Collagen ampoule.* Prepare the client in the normal way, with indifferent pad on the arm, moistened in its special envelope, and attached with a lead to the machine [*Beauty Gallery Face/Body Galvanic Unit*]. Prepare the facial applicator wand or mask method, and apply the Collagen ampoule to the moistened skin, patting in gently. Apply the treatment according to the method chosen — if using the facial applicatory wand, with its disposable cotton wool wad, ensure this is really damp and firmly in place. Check all connections are firm and envelopes, etc., moist to ensure good flow of current from the galvanic system. Apply the facial applicator to the cheek, turn on the galvanic machine, switch to the negative (−) polarity and gradually increase the intensity until the client is aware of the sensation, and natural skin resistance is overcome (which takes about 30 seconds to accomplish, working in one area). As soon as the client is aware of the sensation, or has a metallic taste in her mouth, or the facial applicator wand is causing skin erythema (reddening) to occur tracking along behind the strokes applied, then the skin resistance/intensity is sufficient. This will occur at anything from ½–4 on the milliamp meter, registering resistance in the skin. Application can proceed for 4–8 minutes according to skin reaction created. When the ampoule has penetrated into the skin, after 3–4 minutes at a low current intensity, and the complexion is warm and glowing, having been treated evenly over the entire face and neck, the polarity/intensity control can be returned to zero and 1 or 2 minutes' application given on the positive (+) polarity to tighten and firm the skin. If this effect is not needed, the entire application can be given to the negative (−) penetrating pole. Whichever polarity is being used, the client's sensation, skin reaction, etc., always decides the level of skin resistance/meter reading to be used, and the length of the overall application. There cannot be any fixed intensities or durations, only guidance given, as each client reacts differently to galvanic iontophoresis.

Using the facial mask method of application, very similar actions are accomplished by the Collagen ampoule, and penetration is very even all over the face/neck. Applying the ampoule to the moistened skin, the mask is applied over a liner (both are thoroughly moistened) and electrode pads attached. The indifferent arm pad is identical to the wand method. All connections are checked, and the galvanic iontophoresis penetration applied, 3-4 minutes or less, on the negative polarity, the intensity returned to zero, and 1-2 minutes or less applied using the positive polarity for toning and firming actions if needed. At the conclusion (either method) the skin should be glowing and taut, gently stimulated and warm. No product should remain on the surface of the skin, it should be completely absorbed, having passed into the skin's dermal layers. Treatment is concluded with moisture protection using the *Ivory Moisture Cream* sparingly applied over the face/throat.

For further information see — BEAUTY GUIDE 3: GALVANIC TREATMENT by Ann Gallant.

HOME TREATMENT

Collagen ampoules may be advised within the home routine in association with the *Gallery Line Ivory Range.* They may be used weekly, twice weekly, or daily if the skin requires a concentrated effect for its improvement. The ampoules may be used for 10 days' consecutive application if the skin need is great — such as after sunbathing on holiday, dehydration from incorrect cosmetic care, or ill health. The beauty therapist will advise as to the exact use for individual need. The ampoule is added to the daily skin care routine, either in the morning prior to moisture protection or at night, prior to night cream application.

Morning skin care — Cleanse with *Ivory Cleansing Milk*
— Tone with *Ivory Toning Lotion*
— APPLY COLLAGEN AMPOULE AT THIS STAGE WHEN USED
— Protect with *Ivory Moisture Cream.*

Night skin care — Cleanse with *Ivory Cleansing Milk*
— Tone with *Ivory Toning Lotion*
— *OR APPLY COLLAGEN AMPOULE AT THIS STAGE*
— Nourish with *Ivory Night Cream.*

As an alternative to the *Ivory Night Cream,* the ampoules Oil of Evening Primrose or Jojoba Oil can be applied, for a luxury concentrated treatment effect. The masks *Ivory Face Mask* or *Opal Hydrating Mask* should also be applied on a weekly basis to stimulate the function of the skin.

Ampoules must be kept in a cool temperature out of direct sunlight and opened [with a careful snap of the narrow end] just prior to use.

Some treatment houses are known for ampoules, others not, while some build their treatment suggestions around the use of ampoules alongside special gels, active fluids, and masks, sometimes incorporating the ampoule actually into the mask application itself. When a trend becomes established — as is happening now internationally with the use of ampoules in beauty therapy — it is natural for the larger companies to try to fulfil their customers' demands, and provide good products to do a professional job.

WHERE GALVANISM IS NOT INDICATED

There are certain substances which, though highly effective and active, do not benefit from being applied under galvanic penetration/ionization, and in fact their activity could be destroyed or made less effective by the electrical frequency. Some ampoules themselves are not suitable for using with galvanism — normally the ones for hypersensitive skins. Here it is mainly the effect of the galvanic current on the skin's frail vascular structure that is the restriction, but it can also be that the ingredients themselves enter the sensitive skin so easily to calm and settle, that galvanism is not needed and holds no special advantages to the treatment. In this case the required action is calming, soothing, strengthening of weak capillaries and fragile skin, so galvanism has nothing to add as the capillaries are so close — in fact too close — to the surface already. The product can reach its mark without the help of galvanic penetration, and in this instance galvanism could act as an irritant.

Manufacturers will state whether galvanism is indicated with the ampoules, and the polarity required, and you should be able to rely on their expertise and quality of product. Ampoule therapy is expensive because of the technology that has gone into the formulation of the products, so pick and use ampoules in the clinic and advise ampoules for home care as a real skin treat for the customer. *Ampoule therapy is a special, professional-only advised routine, which only the beauty clinic can apply specifically to the client's needs both in the clinic and in the home.*

KNOW THE SKIN

The therapist's skill lies in her choice for the skin, so her understanding of skin and its behaviour, causes of problems, and its relationship to health, etc., is very essential to success. To get spectacular results you must choose well, and visible changes in the skin should be expected very quickly. A treatment card should show within one or two weekly applications — within the facial routine — a definite improvement and even in stubborn cases such as acne this should normally be evident within 4 to 6 weeks, usually sooner. *Naturally this is with advised home care which the client must follow, and which may include use of ampoules at home as well as normal products.* As a professional, do tell the client what she needs to help her skin, do not leave her suspended in her improvement. She consults you for your expert advice to get a result — only by telling her what she must use at home can these results be assured.

Plan the client's professional treatment record card to provide for a six-treatment reassessment/rediagnosis, to check progress and indicate whether changes are necessary in the overall plan, including ampoule therapy. This is a good pattern to follow in your work, and provides the essential information for home care advice.

So fast results are expected, and occasionally there will be an adverse reaction — as these are very effective routines. By checking contra-indications carefully (reasons why the treatment is unsuitable or may not be given) and working with mild action ampoules initially — such as 'Dehydration' for moisturizing — until skin reactions are known, most over-reactions can be avoided. Most of the over-reaction on the skin comes from using the galvanic current at too high an intensity, or too long within the application, using the manufacturer's suggestions as if they were commandments. The suggestions are only given as guidance, nothing more.

The skin reacts to the improper use of the galvanic frequency, not normally to the ampoules, which have an excellent record of low toxicity and little history of allergic reaction, especially considering their active ingredients and the results they are expected to achieve. So it is usually the application at fault, not the ampoule. Working on the side of caution is always sensible, remembering that low intensity always works better — that is below the discernible level. For it has been noticed that galvanism works by being pulled into the skin, not pushed in. Also it is sensible to do short applications initially until the skin's capacity for both the electrical frequency and the ampoule product is known. Do not forget, it is always the therapist who decides which ampoule to use, how long to apply it, at which intensity/skin resistance to get best results, etc., for only she has the client and her skin in front of her, and can make a correct decision based on watching the skin reaction, and talking to the client for 'feel' and general feedback relating to the application.

GAINING FROM PREVIOUS KNOWLEDGE

It is very useful to have worked on the skin previously before starting ampoule therapy, to get an idea of its sensitivity and reactions to electrical frequencies. Seeing how the client and her skin cope with electro-therapy is also wise, as some clients are just not good with electrical treatments however well applied, and these people should be gently encouraged towards them over several sessions if they would really gain great benefit. Otherwise they could be given alternative routines, perhaps using the ampoules incorporated into masks.

Younger clients really like effective, fast acting, quick result routines. They are not in the clinic to relax but to get a specific result — a clean skin, freedom from blemishes, a clear glowing complexion. Mature clients have to be encouraged on to galvanic routines, and can be if the advantages are stressed, and the ampoule therapy is presented in a very special way — as being of particular benefit, with its effects being hard to match by any other method. One ampoule application, well chosen and carefully applied, is sufficient proof for the client, for she should be able to see visibly different results after just one treatment, if it has been the best one for her personal skin condition. Choosing well, presenting the treatment professionally, showing the client her individual ampoule, explaining why it has been chosen specifically for her skin, and applying it carefully to avoid anxiety, is the whole art of being skilled in this aspect of electro-therapy. *This is advanced work, and should be presented as such — let the client know she deserves a special approach in treatment, make the application a treat for her.*

AMPOULE RANGES AVAILABLE

Ampoule therapy is a fast expanding area of business for the product houses. Though it has been in use in Europe for many years it is only recently that it has become very popular, mainly because of the improvements and advances in the galvanic equipment available and the smoothness and comfort of the frequency on the skin, and the circulatory effects on the body within cellulite routines. It is now known that the less galvanic current used, the greater will be the effect of the ampoules, on the deeper skin layers.

The lower the current intensity is kept, the better the results, and side-effects — over-sensitization of the skin, irritation, etc. — are avoided, allowing product penetration to get to work more successfully. So it is important, once the client has experienced the galvanic current sensation, to lower the intensity to a level where she can scarcely feel it at all, and complete the application in that way.

There are ampoule ranges that are individual — not backed by a related treatment range but able to be used with any complementary product (useful when the client is established and happy with her present home skin care routine). There are others which co-ordinate completely throughout, providing professional treatment products, ampoules, and special masks (sometimes using ampoules themselves in the mask formulae) and these follow through with home products, ampoules, etc., providing the client's every need. This is excellent as it allows no opportunity for incorrect items to be slipped into the home sequence. The therapist provides everything the client needs both professionally and for home use, from the clinic, boosting sales and offering a highly professional service. Then there are those ranges that present a slightly different approach, having a unique system where specially chosen cleansing products, gels, active ampoules, and fluids are formulated specifically for the client by the therapist at the time of treatment. Again a highly professional approach, very impressive to the client and profitable to the salon.

If we look at some of the skin conditions that would benefit from ampoule therapy it is possible to see what a large selection of products are available, to meet these skin conditions. Not all the ampoules mentioned are available all over the world, so the alternatives mentioned can be used. If therapists start asking for ampoules, the distributors will make them available for the industry; it is up to the beauty operators to know what they want, and buy it regularly to make it worth the supplier's while to stock them. Ampoules have a shelf-life of up to two years, being sealed and vacuum formed in glass phials. They are expensive, but remember that the therapist gets the benefit in increased treatment and home sales, plus gains with an overall improvement in facial treatment profitability within the clinic. So all aspects gain: the clinic, the client, and sales profits on product sales.

AMPOULES — REFERENCE LIST
SUPPLIERS AND MANUFACTURERS

Product	Manufacturer or Supplier
GALLERY LINE AMPOULES	GALLERY LINE AMPOULES
Collagen (No 1)	by Ann Gallant
Elastin (No 2)	from
Bio-Regenerator (No 3)	E A Ellison & Co Ltd, Brindley
Placenta (No 4)	Road South, Exhall Trading
Wheatgerm Extract (No 5)	Estate, Coventry CV7 9EP,
Dehydration (No 6)	UK. Tel: (0203) 362505
Active Herbs (No 7)	
Camomile (No 8)	
Ginseng (No 9)	
Royale Jelly (No 10)	
Oil of Evening Primrose (No 11)	
Jojoba Oil (No 12)	
Desincrustation (No 13)	
Collagen & Elastin (No 14)	
Aloe Vera (No 15)	
Cellulite Lotion	
(Jade Body Range)	
ANN GALLANT BEAUTÉ	Esthetic & Beauty Supply
THERAPY AMPOULES	16 Coldwater Road, Don Mills,
Desincrustation	Ontario M3B 1Y7, Canada.
Hydrating Plus	Tel: (416) 444 1154
Collagen & Elastin	There is also a Californian
Active Herbs	office, USA
Camomile Calmer	
Oil of Evening Primrose	
PAULI — VIENNA	W. Pauli, A.1160 Wien, Stoeber-
ANDORA RANGE	platz 5, Austria
IONT-AMPUL	
Active Herbs	England — Elisabeth Peet,
Aloe Vera	Schwarzenberg House,
Anti-Acne	13 Windsor St, Chertsey,
Allergetic	Surrey KT16 8AY
Cellulites	
Couperose	
Gelée Royale	
Ginseng	South Africa — Ann Lang, Her-
Hydro Regulator	bal Beauty Pty Ltd, PO Box
Placenta	93457, Yeoville 2143,
Vitamin	Johannesburg, RSA

REVITA
Collagen & Gelée Royale
Cinara Detox

Rutin & Azulen
Acnex
Gelée Royale & Vit A

England — Elisabeth Peet,
   Schwarzenberg House,
   13 Windsor St, Chertsey,
   Surrey KT16 8AY

West Germany — G Leinberger &
   Co, D-8229 Laufen-
   Mayerhofen Oberbayern

Austria — Goudounex GmbH,
   A-1140 Wien, Diesterwegg 13

Switzerland — Medinca, R.
   Brandenberger & Co,
   CH.—6301 ZUG. Postfach

Holland — Institut RIA de Korte,
   Amsterdam, Nicolaas,
   Witsenstraat 5

Belgium — Revita Importation
   et Distribution, B-1060
   Bruxelles, Avenue Brugman 7

DR HOFMAN IONTOCUTIN
Iontocutin Ampoules 1–6 for
various skin conditions,
mature skin, normalizing
Couperose, for dry skin, acne,
and seborrhoea (desincrustation).
Cellulite for the body.

Dr Hofman GmbH Karlsruhe,
   West Germany.
Iontocutin ampoules — these
well known ampoules are
available from many suppliers
and beauty wholesalers
internationally.

DR R A ECKSTEIN
BIO-KOSMETIK
Ampoule Skin Treatment
Descrustin
Embryo-Kolloid
Kollagen
Tonic F
Tonic S
Tonic Sensitive
Tonic G
Tonic H
Tonic R

Manufacturer — Linde Eckstein,
   Bio-Kosmetik. KG. 8501,
   Oberasbach, Nurnberg,
   West Germany — Dr Eckstein
products and ampoules are
available only from Dr Eckstein
agents around the world. A
complete range of professional
only products, to meet all skin
conditions.

BIODROGA COSMETICS
Ampoules
Special Moisturising Ampoule
Special Soothing Ampoule
Special Collagen Ampoule

Biodroga, Im Rosengarten,
7570 Baden-Baden,
West Germany
Products available from
Biodroga agents around the
world, details from the
manufacturer.

South Africa — Supplier/Agent
— Ann Lang, Herbal Beauty
Pty Ltd PO Box 93457,
Yeoville 2143, Johannesburg,
RSA

R.V.B. NUTURA COSMETICS
T.S. and Multipla Ranges/
Systems
Active Ampoules
153 Ampoule TS1
   Stimulating Vegetable
   Complex
150 Ampoule TS2A. Royal
   Jelly for oily skins
151 Ampoule TS3. Royal
   Jelly for dry skins
155 Ampoule TS4. Moisturiz-
   ing Vegetable Complex
154 Ampoule TS5. Soothing
   Vegetable Complex
152 Ampoule TS6.
   Regenerating Complex

Piana Cosmetici Sp A. Castel
S. Pietro Terme Italia,
(Manufacturer).
R.V.B. products available only
from agents around the world. A
unique system of natural, herbal-
based treatments — active fluids,
creams, and foresis masks
within which the ampoules work
to best effect. Training and
product guidance available
from R.V.B. agents worldwide.

PLUS — MINUS. Aloe Vera
Professional Products
Cleansing Milk — dry/normal
Cleansing Milk — oily/acne
Toner
Cleansing Fluid

Corrective Intercontinental
   Cosmetics, B.V. Overdam 5.
   1081 CE. Amsterdam, Holland
A complete range of professional
products based on aloe vera,
which uses ionization to
complete its effects.

AMPOULE TREATMENT — QUICK CHECK LIST

CONDITION	ACTION REQUIRED	AMPOULE SUGGESTION	POLARITY	MAKE
OVER-ACTIVITY OF THE SKIN Seborrhoea Enlarged pores Over-secretion of oil Blemishes/scars	Deep cleansing with desincrustation and normalizing, to correct over-functioning and improve hydric balance. Also in the case of sensitivity to calm and settle the skin and aid healing process			
Specific Skin Condition Oily and sensitive	Corrective/regulatory/calming	Descrustin	(−)	Dr Eckstein
		Desincrustation	(−)	Gallery Line
		Desincrustation	(−)	Ann Gallant
		Tonic G	(+)	Dr Eckstein
		Active Herbs	(− to +)	Gallery Line
		Active Herbs	(− to +)	Ann Gallant
		Aloe Vera	(− to +)	Gallery Line
		Tonic S	(+)	Dr Eckstein
		Camomile	(No Gal)	Gallery Line
		Camomile Calmer	(No Gal)	Ann Gallant
Oily and normal sensitivity	Corrective/regulatory	Descrustin	(−)	Dr Eckstein
		Desincrustation	(−)	Gallery Line
		Desincrustation	(−)	Ann Gallant
		Tonic G	(+)	Dr Eckstein
		Iontocutin 3	(−)	Dr Hofman
		Active Herbs	(− to +)	Gallery Line
		Active Herbs	(− to +)	Ann Gallant
		Active Herbs	(− to +)	Iont-ampul

CONDITION	ACTION REQUIRED	AMPOULE SUGGESTION	POLARITY	MAKE
Seborrhoea	Corrective/regulatory/refining	Descrustin	(−)	Dr Eckstein
		Desincrustation	(−)	Gallery Line
		Desincrustation	(−)	Ann Gallant
		Iontocutin 3	(−)	Dr Hofman
		Tonic S	(+)	Dr Eckstein
		Active Herbs	(− to +)	Gallery Line
		Active Herbs	(− to +)	Ann Gallant
		Active Herbs	(− to +)	Iont-ampul
		Anti-Acne	(− to +)	Iont-ampul
		Acnex	(No Gal)	Revita
		Royale Jelly	(− to +)	Gallery Line
Thickened, scarred, seborrhoea, cysts, lesions, etc.	Corrective/regulatory, refining/peeling/ healing	Desincrustation	(−)	Gallery Line
		Desincrustation	(−)	Ann Gallant
		Descrustin	(−)	Dr Eckstein
		Iontocutin 3	(−)	Dr Hofman
		Tonic S	(+)	Dr Eckstein
		Active Herbs	(− to +)	Gallery Line
		Active Herbs	(− to +)	Ann Gallant
		Active Herbs	(− to +)	Iont-ampul
		Anti-Acne	(− to +)	Iont-ampul
		Acnex	(No Gal)	Revita
		Iontocutin 5	(+)	Dr Hofman
		Aloe Vera	(− to +)	Gallery Line

CONDITION	ACTION REQUIRED	AMPOULE SUGGESTION	POLARITY	MAKE
OUT OF BALANCE SKIN				
pH disturbed	Requires settling and bringing to correct hydric/pH/and oil balance. (Problem may be related to dietary and health factors.)	Cinara Detox	$\left(\begin{array}{l}\text{½ time }-\\ \text{½ time }+\end{array}\right)$	Revita
Oily & dry patches		Aloe Vera	− to +	Gallery Line
Poor texture		Ginseng	− to +	Gallery Line
Occasional spots/irritation		Camomile	(No Gal)	Gallery Line
		Camomile Calmer	(No Gal)	Ann Gallant
		Aloe Vera	− to +	Iont-ampul
UNDER-FUNCTIONING OF THE SKIN	Hydration, normalizing, skin balancing, regeneration, stimulation			
Dehydrated				
Lacking moisture				
Lifeless				
Atrophic, ageing skin				
Loss of elasticity/skin tone				
Fine lines/softness				
Crepey texture				

CONDITION	ACTION REQUIRED	AMPOULE SUGGESTION	POLARITY	MAKE
Specific Skin Condition Normal to dry, lacking moisture	Hydration, gentle stimulation	Tonic F	(– to +)	Dr Eckstein
		Special moisturising ampoule	(– to +)	Biodroga
		Dehydration	(– to +)	Gallery Line
		Hydrating Plus	(– to +)	Ann Gallant
		Ginseng	(– to +)	Gallery Line
		Hydro Regulator	(+ to –)	Iont-ampul
		Camomile	(No Gal)	Gallery Line
		Camomile Calmer	(No Gal)	Ann Gallant
		Aloe Vera	(– to +)	Gallery Line
		Ginseng	(– to +)	Iont-ampul
		Ginseng	(– to +)	Gallery Line
Dry, needing stimulation (perhaps neglected, overtanned, or caused through ill health, low fat diet, etc.)	Hydration, stimulation, bringing back to balance	Collagen	(– to +)	Iont-ampul
		Collagen	(– to +)	Gallery Line
		Hydro Regulator	(+ to –)	Iont-ampul
		Collagen & Royale Jelly	(No Gal)	Revita
		Oil of Evening Primrose	(No Gal)	Gallery Line
		Oil of Evening Primrose	(No Gal)	Ann Gallant
		Royale Jelly	(– to +)	Gallery Line
		Elastin	(– to +)	Gallery Line

CONDITION	ACTION REQUIRED	AMPOULE SUGGESTION	POLARITY	MAKE
		Bio-Regenerator	(– to +)	Gallery Line
		Tonic R	(– to +)	Dr Eckstein
		Wheatgerm Extract	(– to +)	Gallery Line
Demanding, mature, neglected, or ageing (needing a lot of help)	Stimulation to improve biological function, cellular exchange, and elasticity of skin	Tonic R	(– to +)	Dr Eckstein
		Embryo Kolloid	(–)	Dr Eckstein
		Kollagen	(–)	Dr Eckstein
		Iontocutin 6	(–)	Dr Hoffman
		Collagen & Elastin	(– to +)	Gallery Line
		Collagen & Elastin	(– to +)	Ann Gallant
		Placenta	(– to +)	Gallery Line
		Bio-Regenerator	(– to +)	Gallery Line
		Collagen & Gelée Royale	(No Gal)	Revita
		Wheatgerm Extract	(– to +)	Gallery Line
		Oil of Evening Primrose	(No Gal)	Ann Gallant
		Oil of Evening Primrose	(No Gal)	Gallery Line
		Jojoba Oil	(No Gal)	Gallery Line
		Special Collagen Ampoule	(–)	Biodroga
		Royale Jelly Placenta	(– to +)	Gallery Line
		Placenta	(– to +)	Iont-ampul

CONDITION	ACTION REQUIRED	AMPOULE SUGGESTION	POLARITY	MAKE
Delicate/mature	Gentle stimulation, improvement in function achieved gently without irritation to superficial capillaries	Embryo Kolloid	(−)	Dr Eckstein
		Tonic R	(− to +)	Dr Eckstein
		Kollagen	(−)	Dr Eckstein
		Allergetic	(− to +)	Iont-ampul
		Aloe Vera	(− to +)	Iont-ampul
		Aloe Vera	(− to +)	Gallery Line
		Couperose	(− to +)	Iont-ampul
		Royale Jelly	(− to +)	Gallery Line
		Camomile	(No Gal)	Gallery Line
		Camomile Calmer	(No Gal)	Ann Gallant
		Jojoba Oil	(No Gal)	Gallery Line
		Oil of Evening Primrose	(No Gal)	Gallery Line
		Oil of Evening Primrose	(No Gal)	Ann Gallant
Mature skin needing help to prevent ageing tendencies *or* all types of skin needing activating, stimulating effects, through neglect overtanning, illness, stress, etc., regardless of age.	Stimulation, balancing, improvement of hydric function, tone and texture	Tonic R	(− to +)	Dr Eckstein
		Vitamin	(− to +)	Iont-ampul
		Iontocutin 2	(−)	Dr Hofman
		Ginseng	(− to +)	Iont-ampul
		Ginseng	(− to +)	Gallery Line
		Royale Jelly	(− to +)	Gallery Line
		Wheatgerm Extract	(− to +)	Gallery Line

CONDITION	ACTION REQUIRED	AMPOULE SUGGESTION	POLARITY	MAKE
Also excellent maintenance suggestion to prevent problems occurring in dry skin		Collagen & Gelée Royale	(No Gal)	Revita
		Collagen & Elastin	(– to +)	Gallery Line
		Collagen & Elastin	(– to +)	Ann Gallant
		Gelée Royal & Vitamin A	(–)	Revita
HYPERSENSITIVITY OF THE SKIN Tendancy to irritation. Dilated capillaries reddening, easily stimulated	Main action protection on physically thin skin. Also strengthening of capillaries, improved functioning of skin to help it cope with stresses and strain placed on it. Main action could be considered preventative as well as protective	Special Soothing Ampoule	(No Gal)	Biodroga
		Allergetic	(– to +)	Iont-ampul
		Iontocutin 4	(–)	Dr Hofman
		Tonic H	(No Gal)	Dr Eckstein
		Rutin & Azulen	(–)	Revita
		Tonic Sensitive	(No Gal)	Dr Eckstein
		Camomile	(No Gal)	Gallery Line
		Camomile Calmer	(No Gal)	Ann Gallant
		Aloe Vera	(– to +)	Gallery Line
		(Use without galvanic current if the skin is hypersensitive)		

DIFFERENT WAYS OF USING AMPOULES

Ampoules used as oils for massage within treatment, examples — Dr Eckstein, Gallery Line, Biodroga and Sothys, Ann Gallant Beauté Therapy Ampoules.

Ampoules used within masks, examples — Ella Baché, Revita, Esthoderm, Anne Foucard.

Ampoules mixed with other treatment elements, freeze dried collagen, etc., examples — Esthoderm, Anne Foucard, Sothys.

Ampoules used weekly at home by client, or as required by skin, example — most of the treatment houses: Gallery Line, Iontocutin, Ann Gallant, Dr Eckstein, etc.

Ampoules forming part of special application system, active gels, creams, masks, etc., example — R.V.B. of Italy.

Ampoules used in a series by client at home, giving a daily ampoule to apply, example — Andora Range of Pauli of Austria, with its Andora Active Series which provides collagen, placenta, vitamin, royal jelly, hydro-regulator, used in series, repeated once over 10-day period. For clients with a large need and equivalent finances, to bring fast results.

Ampoules used within treatment in a variety of ways, with and without galvanism to activate. Used independently, mixed with masks, applied after cleansing, as part of cleansing, within massage, after massage, or at the treatment's conclusion. Most treatment houses now use ampoules in some way to provide desired results, follow the manufacturer's instructions as to application method, where in sequence, etc., plus use common sense relying on experiences gained from personal work.

FACE/BODY GALVANIC UNIT

'BEAUTY GALLERY' WITH GALVANIC UNIT

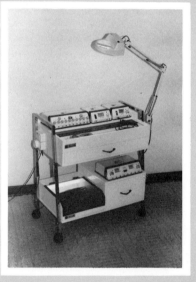

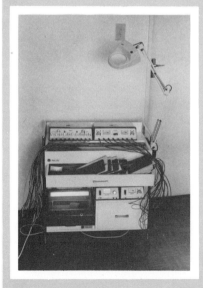

FULL BODY APPLICATION

Where a full body service is offered, the clinic models of the body galvanic system for cellulite and faradic system are necessary. These permit fast and effective results for the treatment of cellulite and for muscle toning

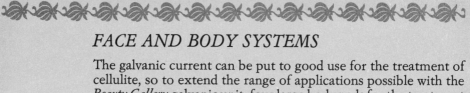

7

Cellulite conditions

FACE AND BODY SYSTEMS

The galvanic current can be put to good use for the treatment of cellulite, so to extend the range of applications possible with the *Beauty Gallery* galvanic unit, four large body pads for the treatment of body cellulite have been included. These permit the treatment of cellulite on the thighs, buttocks or abdominal areas, and are especially useful where specific reduction in one area is required.

If extensive areas of the body suffer from the cellulite problem, the complete body galvanic system for cellulite would be required, which having 8 outlets (16 pads), can treat a large area simultaneously. This saves a great deal of time for the clinic and client, and is essential where a full body service is offered.

The principles of galvanism for treating cellulite are however identical whether 4 or 16 pads/electrodes are used, being based on iontophoresis or penetration of active substances into the tissues to speed fluid loss from the tissues and help the mobilization of fat when the client is on a reduction diet. The client's shape can alter because of the fluid loss even without a change in the overall weight.

Each set of pads or electrodes acts as a pair with differing polarities, one acts as positive, one as negative. The positive electrode is marked by a red connection wire, the negative electrode by a black connection attaching it to the galvanic unit's outlet. So one pad acts as the indifferent electrode, the other as the working electrode, though it has been seen that this polarity can be altered on the machine to change the attracting force of the electrode. It can be designated positive or negative in its polarity according to the effects required, by altering the polarity changer on the galvanic unit.

The process of galvanic iontophoresis for cellulite in body therapy is very similar to that of penetration of active substances in facial therapy. What does differ is the nature of the lotions, emulsions, gels, etc., being employed to treat the cellulite condition, and the action on the cellular tissues to aid the removal of the cellulite problem.

CELLULITE

This is a body condition of ineffective circulation, normally associated with an adipose or fatty tissue deposit in a localized area, which assumes a dimpled skin appearance on compression. It is a very unattractive body problem which can spoil an attractive figure, so the galvanic treatment is a very popular application which can produce excellent results if reinforced by the client's efforts at home. It is a condition considered to be associated with poor body elimination, an inability of the body system to get rid of toxic substances, and a general lack of vitality in the body. It is a problem condition in that it can affect very active people who exercise regularly and are fit, as well as sedentary individuals who do not lead a very healthy or vigorous existence.

Factors such as constipation, incorrect diet (too high in fats, carbohydrates, alcohol, etc.), smoking, lack of exercise/deep and correct breathing, effects of stressful living, poor sleeping patterns, are all considered to have a bearing on the condition. So a full body assessment is needed to resolve the problem. Probably the most important factor overall is *elimination,* aided by a fruit and vegetable and protein diet (classed as an elimination type of diet), and factors which speed the release of the fluids trapped in the cell membranes of the subcutaneous fatty tissue layers. So galvanic treatment is excellent for the problem of cellulite, having a flushing effect on the system when used in combination with anti-cellulite products which have a diuretic effect.

The diuretic or fluid loss effect caused by the penetration of the active lotions under the active pads, causes the client to pass more fluid as urine, and stubborn areas of cellulite disperse over a period of time. The client must have medical advice as to the suitability of the treatment if she has a medical history of kidney infections, infections of the bladder or urinary tract, as the treatment can cause irritation on rare occasions due to the active substances the body is passing through the urine. The client should be warned about the additional water she will pass, so she does not become anxious. This effect will be accelerated if the client uses an anti-cellulite product on the problem area at home, and is also drinking herbal teas to speed her elimination process. Clients with a history of nervous disorders or who have suffered damage to the nervous system (such as pinched nerves, paralysis of a nerve, dermatitis, etc.) should be considered contra-indicated unless medical approval has been given prior to treatment.

APPLICATION

The galvanic cellulite treatment can be applied independently over a clean skin (normally washed and rinsed thoroughly), or used within a 1 hour cellulite routine incorporating peeling, heat, massage, muscle contraction or vacuum suction and galvanism. This treatment is extremely effective in the removal of the cellulite problem, which can be considered a special type of weight condition. The effects of the combined action of stimulation, circulation improvement, interchange of blood and lymphatic fluids, etc., caused by the heat, massage, lymphatic drainage (vacuum), is then flushed away by the effect of the galvanic current penetrating the diuretic, anti-cellulite product into the tissues. The effect of this action when linked with the pumping effect of the faradic current on the muscles as they are exercised, is very effective in removing areas of stubborn adipose tissues.

CONTROLS AND THEIR USE

Negative and positive polarity/ intensity control, milliamp meter. On/Off switch, pilot light. Outlets for electrodes: face (1), body (2). Connection leads: red = positive, black = negative

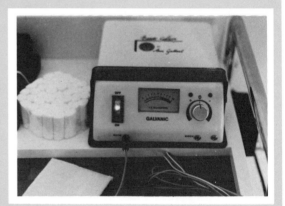

PRODUCTS FOR THE TREATMENT OF CELLULITE

The correct treatment and use of home care products such as Jade *body products from* Gallery Line *are essential for success with cellulite*

The galvanic current plays an important part in this overall elimination process, both by the product penetration, and by causing an interchange of tissue fluids within the cell membrane. It is considered that the galvanic application would still be effective without the cellulite product, because of this interchange effect, but it seems more effective to involve the client in her progress and improvement of the problem, and it centres her attention on to the offending area. Results do appear to be obtained more quickly when a product is applied within the treatment, and the client is made more aware of the effects on her body, and it gets her involved in the whole treatment programme, which is excellent. The client can be shown how to use massage movements on the problem areas, when applying the anti-cellulite product at home, and she may be encouraged to use a friction glove and complementary body products based on citrus extracts, all elements known to aid the circulation and tone the skin.

TREATMENT APPLICATION — INDEPENDENT USE OF GALVANISM, HALF-HOUR

The skin is washed and rinsed thoroughly, and cellulite products massaged in with firm petrissage movements, to increase the circulation slightly. The entire area can be massaged though it is only necessary to apply the ion active product under the active pad. The product must be smoothed into the skin until it disappears, then the covered pads can be applied. The conductive electrodes are enclosed in damp sponge-type envelopes, and then firmly attached to the area with strapping, placing the working active pad over the offending area. All the sponge envelope's surface must be in firm contact with the skin otherwise skin irritation could occur under the pad. The sponge envelopes must be wrung out well.

The indifferent pads are placed in convenient positions, normally on the opposite side of the thigh, or in close proximity to the treatment area. These pads act as the attracting force for the galvanic current, and permit the penetration of the cellulite product to take place under the working electrode. If two areas of the thigh need treatment, these must be dealt with on separate treatment occasions, reversing the working pads, and therefore the treatment area. They should not be treated within the same treatment session as it alters the interchange of tissue fluid and skin irritation could result as well as making the treatment ineffective.

The effective polarity for treating cellulite is the negative polarity. So the inactive pads are the positive polarity, with the active pads the negative, under which penetration will occur to help the tissues to release their trapped fluids into the body's vascular and lymphatic systems.

Remember that the electrodes are only given their polarity from the machine, and initially are determined on a positive setting. The active working electrode starts with a black lead and the indifferent attracting or 'magnet' electrode starts treatment with a red lead.

The main emphasis of the treatment is the negative polarity, which once the pads are in place, is used at a level the client can just feel for 5 to 6 minutes, then the skin resistance is overcome and the product penetrates and is effective. Then the milliamp meter and intensity control are returned to zero, and the opposite polarity used for just a moment or two to cause the tissue fluid interchange effect, at a very low level of skin resistance. It appears to be unnecessary to use the positive polarity for a long application, or at a high intensity, and in fact results seem improved with the level used being well below that at which the client is aware of a sensation.

With several large pads in place the surface area to overcome skin resistance is large, so it is wisest to be guided by the client's reactions to the treatment rather than by the milliamp reading on the meter. In any event a reading of no more than 4 to 5 should ever be needed, if it is remembered how galvanism works, more as an attracting force, using a flow transmission to be effective. So a very low reading may be present on the meter, while the treatment is being perfectly effective. The quality of the skin preparation will also make a lot of difference to how effective the routine is, and what results are obtained over a number of weeks. After the treatment is completed (½ hour in total) the skin can be dried after removing the straps and sponge-covered envelopes containing the pads. The client should be advised not to bath that same day, but rather to permit the treatment to be fully effective in the skin. Results over a period of a few weeks will show a visible change in cm/inches, and if combined with a diet plan, a weight loss will also result. Some of the change of shape is due to the fluid loss, both in the local area and in the body generally, caused by the diuretic action of the combined galvanic application and the active product applied both within treatment and at home.

The application should not be applied to the same area again for a week, though it may be applied in rotation when only a small number of pads are available and the problem is widespread on the client. The thighs, buttocks, and abdominal areas can be treated in turn within a week, on ½ hour treatment sessions. These areas could all be treated at once with a multi-outlet *Beauty Gallery* galvanic body cellulite system, saving a lot of time and making the treatment more effective.

The concentrated cellulite applications incorporating various elements of treatment, heat, massage, vacuum massage, faradism, and galvanism, are very useful where the client has a specific problem, such as the thighs, or is overweight as well as suffering from the cellulite condition. The 1 hour application can be designed to meet the client's specific needs, based on the information gained during the assessment of the figure initially when obtaining the client's personal records, weight, height, muscle tone, fat deposits, posture faults, etc. More time can be given to muscle contraction, less to vacuum suction, etc., if the needs of the body seem to make it necessary. If elimination is a problem, then galvanism can be given prominence in the application, and extra attention given to improving the client's lifestyle, eating habits, etc.

The cellulite routine is very popular with clients because of the results it is possible to obtain, and it has become a standard part of body therapy.

PADDING FOR BODY CELLULITE USING THE 'BEAUTY GALLERY' GALVANIC SYSTEM

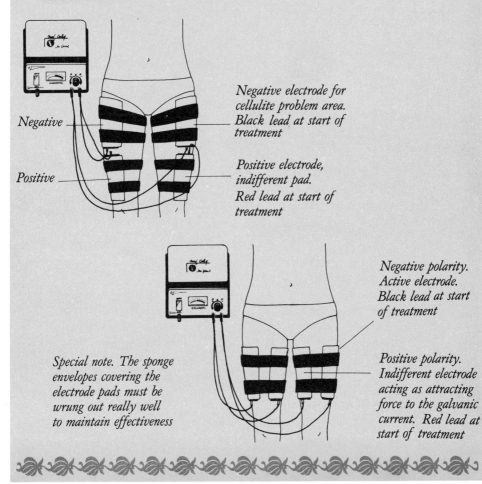

Negative

Positive

Negative electrode for cellulite problem area. Black lead at start of treatment

Positive electrode, indifferent pad. Red lead at start of treatment

Special note. The sponge envelopes covering the electrode pads must be wrung out really well to maintain effectiveness

Negative polarity. Active electrode. Black lead at start of treatment

Positive polarity. Indifferent electrode acting as attracting force to the galvanic current. Red lead at start of treatment

BODY GALVANIC CELLULITE SYSTEM

(a) Full body treatment of cellulite provides fast, effective and profitable results for the clinic

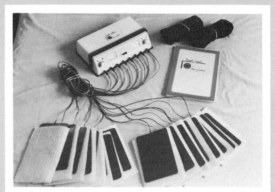

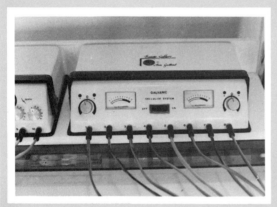

(b) With 8 outlets (16 pads) many cellulite problem areas can be treated at once

(c) The cellulite treatment is very popular with clients as it gives them the results they want

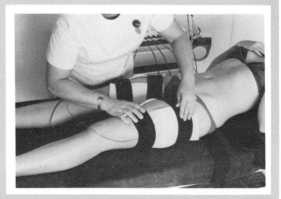

FULL BODY APPLICATIONS

Where a full body service is offered, it will be necessary to have the *Beauty Gallery* body galvanic system for cellulite, as a treatment which can deal effectively with large areas of the body at once. This is a very impressive and effective treatment for cellulite, and brings fast results to eliminate unsightly bulges which particularly affect the thighs, lower buttocks, abdominal area, and occasionally the upper arms. Lumpy dimpled areas, recognized as the cellulite condition, can be replaced by taut, firm, smooth skin, and fluid retention dispersed if it is a circulatory problem, not relating to a physical complaint.

DEALING WITH CELLULITE

The cause of the cellulite problem has been considered and it is evident that if the condition is extensive rather than localized, medical guidance will be necessary to ascertain the client is in good health and suitable for treatment. In many cases a weight loss is indicated, requiring changes to be made in background factors such as diet, exercise and lifestyle.

If on the initial figure assessment the basic problem seems to be one of poor elimination resulting in a cellulite condition, the treatment programme can be coordinated around the galvanic cellulite routines, using them as the basis for the overall success of the slimming plan. Correct diagnosis is therefore important, and measurements, height, muscle tone assessment, areas of fatty or cellulite deposits must all be recorded carefully on the client's treatment record card. These figure points must be discussed with the client to gain her co-operation and willingness to follow the therapist's advice on dietary, exercise, and lifestyle changes.

THE CELLULITE ROUTINE

The cellulite routine is well designed to bring fast results safely, and it can be adapted to suit the client's needs within a 1 hour treatment, combining electrical, manual, and cosmetic product elements. A popular routine includes skin peeling, followed by massage and heat, vacuum suction (lymphatic drainage) or muscle contraction, and concluded by the galvanic application for cellulite using special anti-cellulite products for the penetration by iontophoresis.

The cellulite routine has instant appeal for the client as it really feels as if something is being achieved. This ensures the client's home efforts, which really allow the results to come about, and also long term will help prevent the problem re-occurring. The cellulite treatment gives the client hope that her difficult and

stubborn problem will be resolved, and helps her to understand the cause of the condition and learn about its avoidance.

PLANNING THE CELLULITE PROGRAMME

The cellulite routine combines many aspects of body therapy to gain results, and should be promoted as a plan of 10 to 12 treatments, of 1 hour's duration. Prepayment of the treatment course helps to ensure the regular attendance that is necessary for success. Treatments can be spaced for maximum results. Initially with the multi-pad 8 outlet (16 pads) body galvanic cellulite system, it is desirable to treat the body areas affected only once a week until overall effects are known, as the system is so effective. If no adverse or unwanted effects are forthcoming, treatment can be applied twice weekly if the cellulite problem is a major one, and the client is in good health.

Alternatively, the 1 hour cellulite routine can be interspaced in the slimming plan with associated treatments of ½ an hour or 1 hour's duration, which will reinforce the effects desired but are not so directly connected with fluid loss from the body. These include heating treatments, steam baths, saunas, etc., plus muscle contraction, massage, vacuum suction, vibratory massage and interferential frequencies, all of which have special actions of their own.

These can be chosen according to the individual need of the client, matching the figure diagnosis information with the known action of the treatment, whether it be toning the muscles, helping fat mobilization, or improving biological function in the tissues.

Factors that will guide the therapist in her treatment planning include the initial size of the client and the condition of her body, her age and overall health, the nature of the subcutaneous weight — fluid fat, hard deposits, swollen dimpled fatty deposits — and the general sensitivity of the skin. Contra-indications also play a part, limiting many of the applications in the older woman, or requiring adaptation of the routine — varicose veins being a major problem.

EFFECTIVE ROUTINES

As these are *active* and *effective* routines, there will be a small proportion of clients who will react to cellulite programmes. Reactions include skin irritation, soreness of the skin in the treatment area, and an excessive loss of fluid as urine or discomfort in passing water. Care over checking the contra-indications or treatment and applying the treatment cautiously at first eliminates many of the problems, but it is still possible to get an extreme reaction even when every reasonable care has been taken.

Once clients realize the effectiveness of these cellulite galvanic routines they tend to want to push in as much treatment as possible, for all they want is the result as quickly as possible. So therapists must guide as to how often the treatment can successfully be given, without getting any unwanted effects. If no bad reactions occur, treatment can be given twice weekly, and the client will immediately notice a change in cm/inches, and will be able to discern a change in the tissues in the affected cellulite areas. Unless a diet is being followed there may not at this stage be any change in the client's weight, but she will look and feel different. The system is being flushed and prepared for the diet to take effect.

INVOLVING THE CLIENT

The initial emphasis should be placed on encouraging the client to believe in the clinic routines and their effects, and to understand how effective she can be in helping herself to cure her problem with professional guidance. Anything that helps in this re-education process should be used, whether it is the application of an anti-cellulite product range at home, use of friction gloves, ivy extract bath products, etc., or the careful attention to diet to aid elimination and help the weight loss. Clients who are close to their ideal weight can even be encouraged to lose a little more to aid the elimination process, and can be advised that the body will naturally regulate itself back to the ideal weight after the treatment plan is successfully concluded.

Every encouragement should be given to getting fit, with sports exercise, general mobility and breathing exercises, or free movement dance-types of exercise, whichever the client would enjoy and be interested to do to help herself. Cutting down on smoking and drinking over the period also helps in this fitness approach, and the client may well be amazed how well she begins to feel with even a few small changes in her lifestyle. Lack of real physical exercise does seem to be a very relevant factor in the formation of cellulite, as also does stress, so if a client can be encouraged to do some exercise she finds enjoyable, whether it be swimming, dancing, gardening, or even walking, this helps in several ways.

The cellulite treatments offered by the therapist act more as a catalyst, providing encouragement and hope for the client, and providing an opportunity for her to learn more about the body problem from the trained therapist.

THE PROBLEM OF CELLULITE

The question of whether a client has cellulite or not, or is simply overweight, remains a controversial one, but the term is a convenient one for describing problem areas of the body marred by dimpling, a swollen appearance and excess adipose tissue. The condition can be soft with loose skin, or hard and compacted as if the tissues are overstretched and swollen. Both descriptions obviously have an involvement with poor muscle tone in the loose skin condition, often termed soft cellulite, and the excess weight or fatty tissue in the compacted condition, known as hard cellulite. So the client may also have weak muscles and really be over-weight, but if she believes that her problem is a cellulite one, then a cellulite routine should be offered, for it is necessary for the client to believe in her chances of improvement.

Once the client starts her treatment programme, whichever aspect needs the most attention can be given it, whether it be overall reduction, muscle toning, lymphatic drainage or galvanic applications for fluid removal. A plan can be devised which includes all these elements, but which centres attention to the offending cellulite areas to keep the client's interest alive.

SOFT AND HARD CELLULITE

If the cellulite condition is not linked with overweight problems, it may well be due to slackness of certain muscles which are hard to exercise fully, such as the inside thigh, upper inside arm and outside or lateral areas of the thigh. These muscles can then develop soft fat deposits over them, and the problem is one of firming and elimination in localized areas. These muscles can be weak even in a very active slim person, and a cellulite condition may appear to be present. This is because these muscles do not have to work hard unless specifically exercised by active routines or by muscle contraction (faradism) in the clinic. In normal life these muscles function under the superior strength of the bigger muscle groups near them, and they only assist movements, they do not instigate them.

The abdominal muscles in women are a prime example of muscles working to support movements rather than to start them, hence the problem with slackness, cellulite or soft fat deposits, and abdominal protrusion in many cases. The abdominal muscles do not have to work hard and can get away with being very lazy. Both galvanic cellulite routines and muscle contraction is needed to solve the problem, backed up by vacuum suction and vibratory massage.

The buttocks can suffer similar problems although these are anti-gravity muscles like the thighs (quadriceps at the front, hamstrings at the back), and all are concerned with keeping the body upright and so are in constant daily use. These areas are more prone to simple weight deposits, and so dietary emphasis would be needed,

but a routine for hard cellulite would still be effective as it aids elimination.

So it is evident that many conditions of poor circulation, weak muscle tone, lumpy skin, or simply weight deposits can all be described as cellulite, if on compression they show the classic orange skin pitting, dimpling and lumpy appearance associated with cellulite. So perhaps it should be considered a form that fat takes in certain areas of the body, and dealt with in that way,

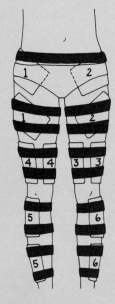

PADDING FOR HEAVY CELLULITE ON THE LEGS

Padding for the back of the body

PADDING SPLIT BETWEEN TWO CLIENTS

Each 4 outlets (8 pads) section is individually controlled for skin resistance and polarity

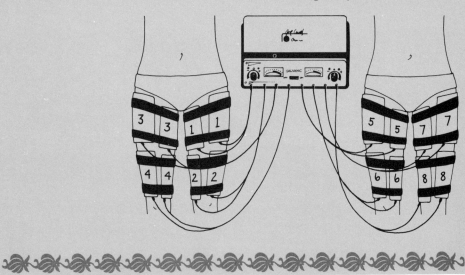

needing a special approach, just as any other difficult body condition does. Certainly diet alone does not always appear to remove the problem, but rather a combination of things seems necessary — galvanism being one of the most useful. With the cellulite routine applied regularly, the affected areas soon change appearance, improving in skin texture, firmness, and bringing about a difference the client can really feel and see for herself.

FULL BODY PADDING

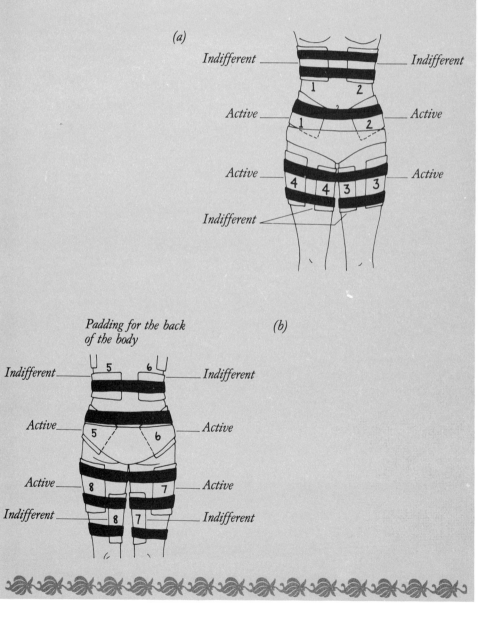

(a)

Indifferent ——— *Indifferent*

Active ——— *Active*

Active ——— *Active*

Indifferent ———

Padding for the back of the body

(b)

Indifferent ——— *Indifferent*

Active ——— *Active*

Active ——— *Active*

Indifferent ——— *Indifferent*

(c)

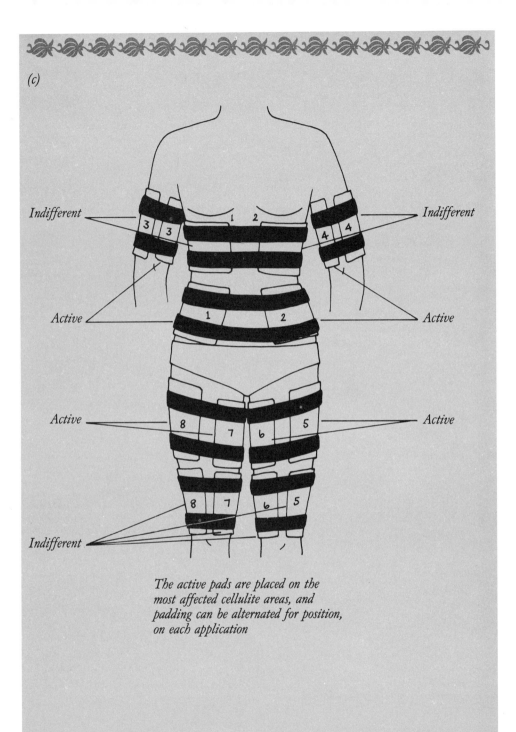

The active pads are placed on the
most affected cellulite areas, and
padding can be alternated for position,
on each application

97

8

Cellulite treatments

HALF-HOUR APPLICATION

The galvanic cellulite system can be applied as an independent treatment, taking ½ an hour in total to apply. Many areas of the body can be treated at once. The 8 outlet system with its 16 large body pads allows full treatment of the body, and these areas can be controlled in two groups, the 4 outlets being controlled on one polarity control, and having their own milliamp meter to show skin resistance under the working electrodes. This can permit the treatment of two areas of the body with slightly different skin resistance readings on the meters, or can provide for two clients to be treated side by side if their problems are not so extensive. Body therapy treatments are becoming more and more communal, and the practice of supervising several clients at once is becoming a standard way of improving profitability in the clinic. Younger clients seem to like this method of treatment, and as long as at all times the client is receiving adequate care and attention to ensure successful and safe treatment, it is a perfectly acceptable practice.

The treatment can be offered in a very similar manner to muscle contraction routines within slimming courses, giving 10 to 20 treatments over a 6 week to 2 month period. It can be applied once or twice a week, depending on the client's reactions, and can be alternated with muscle contraction or vibratory massage/vacuum suction. It is useful to give treatment of some sort three times a week, as this keeps the client's interest high, and provides for checking on the diet and encouraging the client on her home efforts.

Treatment is then applied as a short duration routine, requiring only skin washing, rinsing, application of the cellulite product, and application of the galvanic iontophoresis for cellulite for a 10 to 15 minute period. The whole treatment can be completed in ½ an hour, and uses very large pads to allow penetration of the active ions into the skin. It is effective applied in this way, and clients will notice a change in the skin and tissues, plus changes in the quantity of urine passed due to the diuretic action of the galvanism and cellulite product.

With all galvanic applications for cellulite it is important that the active anti-cellulite products drawn into the tissues remain there and are not altered by bathing, etc., that day. Also the client must use the products at home to maintain the diuretic effect.

ONE-HOUR TREATMENT

Results can be quite dramatically improved if the galvanic body system for cellulite is developed into a special routine for cellulite — an entire treatment devised to maximize the elimination effects of the routine, aid skin texture, and remove the offending skin dimpling and pitting associated with the condition.

Attracting the client into the clinic with the instant appeal of a special cellulite treatment provides the ideal opportunity to discuss all the other elements involved, diet, exercise, adequate rest and relaxation, etc., so it is valuable in more ways than one. The important thing is to attract the client in so that she can be helped, and the cellulite treatment appears very popular with clients as it is so comprehensive with manual, electrical, and product applications, and is also well known for gaining results.

CELLULITE ROUTINE APPLICATION

All the equipment that will be required is prepared and placed in readiness. The client is helped on to the couch after measurements are taken, and made comfortable according to the area to be treated. Protective sheeting can be placed over the couch to help avoid soiling and to speed the cleaning up procedures. Treatment commences with a small amount of body peeling product applied on to the dampened treatment area, e.g. the thighs, and this is worked into a thin lather with brisk petrissage friction movements. This stimulates the circulation and deep-cleanses the skin. After a few minutes' massage, the body peeler is removed using towels wrung out in hot water, and twisted into loops to permit speedy wiping of the area. The towels must be rinsed and the area wiped briskly until completely free from the peeling product. The body peeler removes dead skin cells and frees the surface from natural oils which could block the action of the muscle contraction and the galvanic iontophoresis concluding the routine. So the skin and tissues are clean and warm, and therefore receptive to the elimination process, toning procedures, and the transference of active substances designed to free fluid trapped in the surface cells.

PEELING AND PREPARATION

(a) The working area is protected, and a thin film of peeling product applied to the cellulite affected area

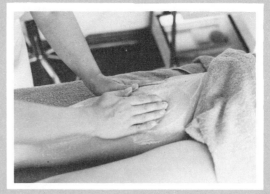

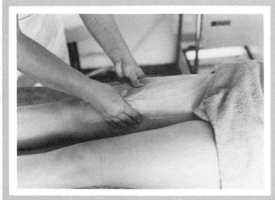

(b) Brisk rolling, friction movements are used to stimulate the circulation and deep-cleanse the skin, to break down skin resistance to electrical current

(c) The body peeler is removed with hot towels, wrung out and twisted into loops to allow fast cleansing of the area. Rinse and repeat briskly until all traces of product are gone

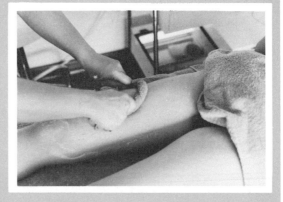

MASSAGE AND HEAT

This stimulation is hastened by massage and heat, using all those movements which improve circulation by physical response — intermittent pressure movements, petrissage, or compression in all its many forms, kneading, rolling, etc., linked with effleurage, stroking movements. The massage should be firm and deep but not vicious, and is a very skilled aspect of the routine, helping to free the adipose tissue and retained fluid (oedema-swelling), thus making them available to the body's vascular and lymphatic circulation for natural removal from the body, or to be used up by the body as fuel. This helps the body's natural functioning, which seems a basic element in the cellulite condition. Smooth, deeply-applied pressure movements towards the inguinal and subinguinal lymphatic nodes in the groin should interlink the general petrissage massage movements, and a change in skin colour should be evident, like a flushing effect.

Working under an infra-red ray lamp hastens the process of elimination, and through warmth relieves any discomfort or spasm in the muscles, so improving the client's capacity for the deeply applied massage. Through the counter-irritation effect of the infra-red rays, subcutaneous blood is brought to the skin's surface, causing a tissue fluid interchange effect, which supports the manual work. At this stage the area is red and very warm, and when this degree of erythema (skin redness) is reached, the limb or area may be kept warm with towels and the heat lamp, and the second limb massaged. If a combined application of the buttocks and thigh is undertaken, the front of the thighs should be treated, and then the back of the thighs and the buttocks brought up to the same stage.

This heat and massage stage of the sequence need only take 10 to 15 minutes in all, due to the fast response gained from the heat lamps and the peeling preparation. Variety can be given to this section of the routine by use of suction apparatus for lymphatic drainage, employing both pulsed static vacuum and the normal gliding method, checking first that the client has no local contra-indications such as varicose veins. Vacuum suction is especially useful if the client has hard fat deposits, and does not appear to suffer from weakness in the muscles, but is simply well padded in the area. It can in fact replace the muscle contraction in the routine if felt to be more useful to the actual problem. Normal lymphatic drainage patterns are followed for the gliding strokes of the vacuum, working to the back of the knees (popliteal nodes) and the groin for the thighs and buttocks (inguinal and subinguinal nodes). Static pulsing must be followed by gliding vacuum strokes working to the lymphatic nodes for this aspect to be effective.

MASSAGE AND HEAT

(a) Massage is used to hasten elimination using petrissage, compression movements, initially working gently to avoid discomfort on the cellulite areas

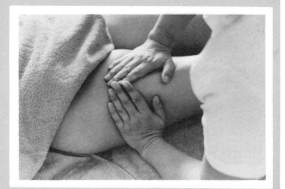

(b) Deep kneading is used firmly and deeply to improve biological functioning in the area, and speed dispersal of the cellulite condition

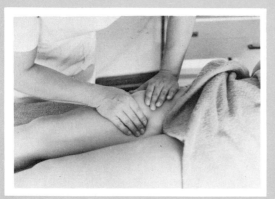

(c) Effleurage, stroking movements are used to link strokes and relieve any discomfort or spasm in the muscles. Heat lamps and vacuum massage can be used to vary the routine

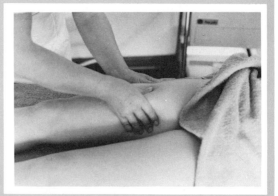

If oil has been used in the massage it must be washed off very carefully with liquid soap and water, and rinsed well with warm towels, otherwise it will prevent good faradic contractions, being a very effective blocker. Fluid-based products, gels, etc., may be used as a lubricant for the massage, which improve the conductivity of the skin to the muscle contraction, reducing its resistance. These save a lot of time in the routine, avoiding the need for cleansing again. Any fluid-based body lotion will be satisfactory.

MUSCLE CONTRACTION

The next stage is muscle contraction, using the multi-outlet faradic system or interferential system, concentrating on those muscles in the most affected areas. These are likely to be the adductors of the inside thigh — which can be exercised as part of a general padding or more specifically and effectively along their length. Also the vastus lateralis — outside thigh — which naturally forming part of the quadriceps (four part) group has to be exercised as one of this group in a general toning padding layout. This also helps the tensor fascia latae (sheet-like fascia) muscle at the top of the outer thigh, which is difficult to treat or exercise naturally. On the buttocks the gluteus maximus and medius are treated, normally with fairly specific padding layouts and reinforced padding if the muscle tone is very poor, or the client rather large.

The treatment sensation should be explained to the client, so that she is not anxious about the application. If the muscular tissues are relaxed, moist, and warm with blood fluid present in large quantities close to the skin's surface, the contractions will be strong, comfortable and effective, and will be achieved with very low intensity levels. So only 10 minutes of contraction will be required to gain the desired effect. Even if the muscles are not really weak, it is still a very useful treatment to apply, as it has excellent side-effects on the functioning of the muscles, and

MUSCLE CONTRACTION/GALVANIC CELLULITE TREATMENT

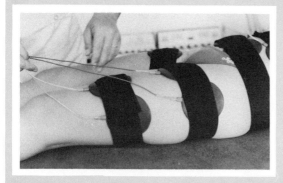

(a) The oil is removed very thoroughly and muscle contracting applied, working to clear motor point placings along the length of the muscles. Only 10 minutes of active contractions needed

(b) The faradic pads are removed and the cellulite product massaged thoroughly into the skin, particularly in the areas where the damp galvanic pads are to be applied

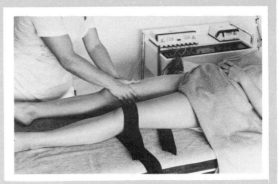

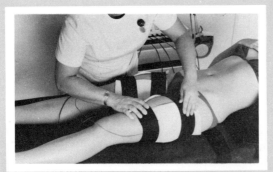

(c) The paired galvanic pads are applied in their envelopes, placing the active pad over the worst areas. The negative pole is applied for 5 to 6 minutes, adjusted to client comfort, polarity returned to zero and the positive pole used for 3 to 4 minutes. So treatment starts with the black lead going to the working pad (cellulite area) and the red lead going to the indifferent pad acting as the magnet

through its pumping effects on the circulation, helps the elimination process as well.

Padding must be efficiently applied, with everything to hand to avoid time wasting in this section. Likewise the next stage — the galvanic cellulite application — the system, pads, sponge envelopes, anti-cellulite product and straps should all be prepared beforehand to permit a fast application.

GALVANIC IONTOPHORESIS

Once again the routine for the cellulite application is based on the principles of iontophoresis for penetration of active substances into the tissues. When treating large body areas it is necessary to be well organized and have a plan of application worked out, to decide where the pads can be most effectively placed and the quickest method of getting them in place to do their work.

The large galvanic pads are prepared, and the sponge envelopes are moistened and wrung out really well, and the pads placed within them. The necessary pairs of pads are prepared and connected to the positive and negative connection leads, which are plugged firmly into the *Beauty Gallery* body galvanic system's outlets. Once ready these pairs of pads can be placed in the storage area in front of the machine on the gallery unit, so that they can be applied very swiftly with the minimum disruption to the client.

The anti-cellulite product is massaged into the area to be treated until it disappears, and the large pads applied in pairs, with the active pad/electrode over the area requiring the greatest effect. For a large client, several pairs of pads can be applied, 4 on each thigh/leg area, 4 on the abdominal area, and 4 on the buttocks and back thigh area. Any combination of padding is acceptable, as long as the pads are in pairs, and they do not overlap each other.

The pads can be quickly strapped into place, either following the cellulite product application in each area, or totally strapped, after application of the product to all affected areas. The pads and straps can be applied together using the straps to hold the pads closely to the body while they are being finally positioned. The pads can be placed side by side, opposite each other, or pointing in the same direction. They may also be angled to fit the contours of the area, for it has to be remembered that their task is to bring about the penetration of the active substances into the areas of the body suffering from the cellulite problem. The indifferent pads are the attracting force, which causes the active product to be drawn into the skin under the active working pads. So the application does not relate to muscle positions, lymphatic nodes, etc., but rather to penetration of products into the skin for diuretic effects on the body, and an improvement of elimination actions on the fluid retained in the body. The galvanism works on the interchange of tissue fluids, brought about by the application of differing polarities, which alter the functioning of the subcutaneous tissues.

DIFFERENCES IN SKIN RESISTANCE

Areas of the body likely to present different levels of skin resistance or sensitivity can be connected to one section or other of the galvanic system outlets, for example, 8 pads could be used on the legs, and 8 on the softer tissues of the trunk. As a very low level of intensity is needed to create a good flow transmission, the difference in skin resistance in different areas of the body is likely to be small, but it could be important for client comfort. Also if the galvanic machine is being shared between two clients of different weight and skin sensitivities at the same time, this control is essential.

APPLYING THE POLARITY

When all the pads are applied, firmly strapped, and correctly connected, the galvanic treatment can proceed with the polarity switched first to the *negative* polarity. The intensity/polarity control is very gradually increased, and having very little skin resistance to overcome will quickly bring about penetration of the cellulite product. Due to the slow build-up effect of the current, built into the *Beauty Gallery* galvanic system to improve client comfort, the client may initially feel very little sensation.

The polarity control can be very gradually increased, guided by client sensation, and pausing for a few seconds at a level the client is only just aware of, with slight prickling in the skin. This allows the skin resistance to be overcome comfortably, and avoids the need for high levels of galvanic current to be used. Then the intensity can be increased carefully to a level the client can just feel as tingling in the skin, which could vary as a reading from 1 to 4 on the milliamp meter registering the skin resistance under the body pad areas. This will depend on the client's build, the type of cellulite or fat present, whether it is hard or soft, plus other factors such as skin sensitivity.

Once again the client's reaction and the sensation she experiences are the main factors which determine the level at which the treatment is applied. It is not necessary for the client to feel it strongly for it to be effective, but it involves her in the routine if at some stage she can feel something working within her skin. It is useful to bring the skin resistance up to a level the client can feel, then slightly reduce this level, for the 5 to 6 minute application time. Once the negative polarity has been completed, which is the most important part of the application, the polarity control can be gradually reduced to the zero point, and increased on the positive polarity for a further few minutes on a very low level of skin resistance.

Applying the positive polarity for a few minutes permits the interchange of tissue fluids to take place in the subcutaneous skin layers, but it does not need to be applied for very long or at a very high level of intensity/skin resistance, and in this way still seems to be very effective. This also reduces the risk of skin irritation, which can occur if a positive polarity is used at too high a level. Normally 3 to 4 minutes at a level the client can hardly feel proves quite adequate, and in most cases a milliamp meter reading of well under 4 is desirable.

After the conclusion of the application the skin may look pink and feel warm with a good degree of erythema, but it should not be irritated or have any raised or sore areas. If these occur they are like a tissue reaction, and the intensity has been too high. This may be due to following the reading on the meter rather than being guided by the client's reactions, sensation felt, etc. It could also point to poor skin preparation, oil or soap left in the tissues, or poor skin contact due to loose strapping or over-dry sponge coverings over the pads, preventing a good flow transmission.

DIURETIC ACTION OF CELLULITE PRODUCTS

The cellulite products applied in this way stay in the tissues long enough to be effective in mobilizing the trapped fluid and fatty tissue which appears to be there as a result of poor and ineffective circulation. This makes these unwanted deposits available to the body, the fat to be used up as energy when the person is on a reduced food intake, and the fluid to be flushed away through the body's normal elimination processes. It is not desirable that the cellulite product should pass directly into the bloodstream and be eliminated with other body wastes too quickly before it has had a chance to be effective. This will happen in time naturally but ideally the active product should stay where the skin and tissues can use them — in the problem areas under the skin.

The entire application for galvanic current within the cellulite routine will not exceed 15 minutes, so the entire cellulite treatment can be accomplished within an hour, if time is not wasted by poor preparation, and lack of skill in padding up and client handling. The therapist will be busy for the whole hour, and the client will feel she has had her money's worth. The treatment concludes with the deft removal of the pads, drying the skin carefully, and the application of a light dusting of talc for comfort, applied with a few gentle effleurage movements. This prevents the skin feeling uncomfortable and helps to re-establish the personal touch aspects of this rather technical treatment.

The cellulite product must remain in the skin to be effective, and the client advised not to bath that same day to gain maximum benefit. Regular use of the cellulite product daily or twice or three times a week, according to skin and body reactions observed initially, will reinforce the professional work and centre the client's attention on her problem. Suitable products include Body Peeler, Body Wash, Massage Oil, Body Lotion and Cellulite Lotion from the *Gallery Line Jade Body Range* by Ann Gallant.

The cellulite product can be applied at night or in the morning after bathing or showering when the skin is receptive and will accept the product willingly. If the fluid loss in the urine becomes excessive the application can be applied less often in the week. The client should also be advised to take in her normal fluid levels, ideally as water, natural fruit juice, etc., rather than as coffee, tea, or fizzy drinks. She must be advised not to restrict her fluid intake in any way, but to drink normally. It should be explained that it is the process of elimination that is at fault, and if the body, through improved functioning, can eliminate all the fluid it does not need for maintaining its hydric balance, it will become very healthy. As well as ridding herself of cellulite, problems such as varicose veins, indigestion, constipation, etc., will all improve naturally. The body will get into good health and the client will not only get into good shape and looks but will feel better in every way.

PLANNING THE CELLULITE PROGRAMME

Cellulite treatments, like all body routines, need to be applied regularly for success, and should be promoted as a plan of 10 to 12 treatments, whether the 1 hour cellulite routine is applied or the ½ hour galvanic application is given independently.

With the larger galvanic cellulite systems, it is advisable to treat the body only once a week until the effects are known. If no adverse results occur, the routine can be applied twice weekly if the problem is a major one. Or, the 1 hour cellulite routine can be interspaced in the slimming plan with associated treatments such as ½ hour muscle contraction, vibratory massage, etc., which reinforce the effects that are not so directly connected with fluid loss from the body.

Factors that will guide the therapist in her treatment planning include the client's age, overall size, general health, and contra-indications. Contra-indications may limit the range of applications in the older woman, especially circulatory problems, high blood pressure, varicose veins, etc., and clients must know the state of their health before commencing treatment.

CHECK LIST FOR CELLULITE TREATMENTS

(1)   Make sure the skin is very clean and free from oil before applying the galvanic current.

(2)   The main action of the cellulite galvanic application is the negative polarity — this is the penetrating pole.

(3)   When the equipment's polarity is determined or set on the positive, the active working electrode starts with a *black* lead, and the indifferent attracting electrode starts with a *red* lead.

(4)   The application only has to follow the simple instructions shown in the Guide and results will be forthcoming. There is really nothing complicated about galvanism once its action is fully understood.

(5)   Changing the polarity of the pads is achieved via the controls of the equipment, which reverse their action.

(6)   If the client gets strong tissue reaction, check the moistness of the pads, and their contact with the skin; the intensity of current/skin resistance could be too high; reduce the amount of time and intensity used with the positive pole.

(7) Wait to find out how the client responds to the galvanic cellulite applications physically, before building too many into her figure improvement programme — these are active routines.

(8) Always give the greater emphasis in treatment to the negative pole.

(9) Galvanism affects the subcutaneous tissues. The active elements penetrating through the intact skin pass into the blood circulation gradually and are excreted by the body — just in the same way as any other form of foreign matter.

(10) Establish the client on a programme of home product use, for example: Body Peeler, Body Wash, Massage Oil, Body Lotion and Active Anti-cellulite Lotion from the Jade Cellulite Range from Gallery Line. Results will be forthcoming as the client will be involved with her own improvement and will make the necessary changes to her lifestyle.

(11) Encourage a change of attitude in the client towards her body condition. Let her know it lies within her power to improve her figure, health and vitality, particularly with the help of the professional therapist who can advise on treatments and products available.

Useful Addresses

PROFESSIONAL ORGANIZATIONS AND EXAMINATION BOARDS

Further information on courses is available from the following examination boards and professional organizations:

Aestheticians' International Association Inc,
5206 McKinney, Dallas, Texas, USA

American Electrolysis Association,
Corresponding Secretary Sandi Strum, 211 Jonnet Building,
4099 William Penn Highway, Monroeville P.A. 15146, USA

Beauty Education International — Beauty Club
Ann Gallant, Forum, Stirling Road, Chichester PO19 2EN, UK

E A Ellison & Co Ltd, Brindley Road South,
Exhall, Coventry CV7 9EP, UK Tel (0203) 362505

Esthetic and Beauty Supply, 16 Coldwater Road, Don Mills,
Ontario M3B 1Y7, Canada Tel (416) 444 1154
There is also a Californian office, USA

British Association of Beauty Therapy and Cosmetology,
Secretary Mrs D. Parkes, Suite 5, Wolesley House,
Oriel Road, Cheltenham GL50 1TH, UK

British Association of Electrolysis,
16 Quakers Mead, Haddenham, Bucks HP17 8EB, UK

British Biosthetic Society,
2 Birkdale Drive, Bury, Greater Manchester BL8 2SG, UK

City and Guilds of London Institute,
46 Britannia Street, London WC1 9RG, UK

Le Comité Internationale D'Esthétiques et de Cosmetologie, (CIDESCO),
CIDESCO International Secretariat, PO Box 9, A1095 Vienna,
Austria

Confederation of Beauty Therapy and Cosmetology,
Education Secretary Mrs B. Longhurst, 3 The Retreat, Lidwells
Lane, Goudhurst, Kent, UK

Institute of Electrolysis,
251 Seymour Grove, Manchester M16 0DS, UK

International Aestheticians' Association,
2304 Monument Boulevard, Pleasant Hill, California 94523,
USA

National Federation of Health and Beauty Therapists,
  PO Box 36, Arundel, West Sussex BN18 0SW, UK

International Therapy Examination Council,
  3 The Planes, Bridge Road, Chertsey, Surrey KT16 8LE, UK

The Northern Institute of Massage,
  100 Waterloo Road, Blackpool FY4 1AW, UK

Skin Care Association of America,
  16 West 57th Street, New York, NY, USA

South African Institute of Health and Beauty Therapists,
  PO Box 56318, Pinegowrie 2123, South Africa

EQUIPMENT MANUFACTURERS

Ann Gallant Beauté Therapy Equipment,
  Esthetic and Beauty Supply, 16 Coldwater Road, Don Mills,
  Ontario M3B 1Y7, Canada, Tel (416) 444 1154
  There is also a Californian office, USA

Beauty Gallery Equipment by Ann Gallant,
  E. A. Ellison & Co Ltd, Brindley Road South,
  Exhall, Coventry CV7 9EP, UK, Tel (0203) 362505

Colne Development Co Ltd,
  2 Station Road, Twickenham, Middlesex, UK

Cristal (Equipment),
  86 Rue Pixérécourt, 75020 Paris, France

Depilex Ltd and Slimaster Beauty Equipment Ltd,
  Regent House, Dock Road, Birkenhead, Merseyside L41 1DG,
  UK

Electro-Medical Services,
  Bermuda Road, Nuneaton, Warks, UK

George Solly Organization Ltd,
  James House, Queen Street, Henley on Thames, Oxon, UK

Soltron Solarium and Sun Beds,
  Josef Kratz, Vertriebsgesellschaft mbH Rottbitzer Straße
  69-5340 Bad Honnef 6 Tel 02224/818-0 Telex jk 8861194

Nemectron Belmont Inc,
  17 West 56th Street, New York, NY10019, USA

Silhouette International Beauty Equipment,
  Kenwood Road, Reddish, Stockport, Cheshire SK5 6PH, UK

Slendertone Ltd,
  12-14 Baker Street, London W1M 2HA, UK

Taylor Reeson Ltd,
  96-98 Dominion Road, Worthing, Sussex, UK

TREATMENT PRODUCT SUPPLIERS

Ann Gallant Beauté Therapy Products,
Esthetic and Beauty Supply, 16 Coldwater Road, Don Mills,
Ontario M3B 1Y7, Canada
There is also a Californian office, USA

Elizabeth of Schwarzenberg,
13 Windsor Street, Chertsey, Surrey KT16 8AY, UK

Clarins (UK) Ltd,
(Oils and body products)
150 High Street, Stratford, London E15 2NE, UK

Gallery Line by Ann Gallant, Skin Care and Body Products,
E. A. Ellison & Co Ltd, Brindley Road South,
Exhall, Coventry CV7 9EP, UK

Pier Augé Cosmetics,
Harbourne Marketing Associates, Oak House,
271 Kingston Road, Leatherhead, Surrey, UK

Thalgo Cosmetic/Importex,
(Marine based products)
5 Tristan Square, Blackheath, London SE3 9UB, UK

MAGAZINES AND TRADE PUBLICATIONS

Beauty Club by Ann Gallant
(International club for all those involved in the beauty industry —
publications/fact sheets/guides/books, etc.)

Details from:
Beauty Education International, Forum, Stirling Road,
Chichester PO19 2EN, UK
Telex 86402, CHITYP G. Ref GALLANT

Ellison, Brindley Road South, Exhall Trading Estate,
Exhall, Coventry, UK Tel 0203 362505

Esthetic and Beauty Supply, 16 Coldwater Road, Don Mills,
Ontario M3B 1Y7, Canada Tel (416) 444 1154
There is also a Californian office, USA

Health and Beauty Salon Magazine

Hair and Beauty Magazine

Hairdresser's Journal

Trade publications for the Hair and Beauty Industries,
details from International Business Press, Quadrant House,
The Quadrant, Sutton, Surrey, UK
(Health and Beauty Salon Magazine Editor — Ms Marion
Mathews) Tel 01 661 3500

Skin Care Magazine,
The National Journal of Esthetics
140 Main Street, El Segundo, California 90245, USA

Cosmetics Magazine
Specialist magazine for all those involved with the sales of
cosmetics, toiletries, make-up, skin and nail care etc.
Beauty Industries Publications Ltd, Suite 201, 801 York Mills
Road, Don Mills, Ontario, Canada

International Hair and Beauty Route
Specialist Magazine for Electrologists, Skin Care and
Esthetics, Beauty Therapists, Editor Mr. D. Copperthwaite
PO Box 313, Port Credit Postal Station, Mississauga,
Ontario, Canada

EQUIPMENT DESIGN AND DEVELOPMENT

Beauty Educational International
Design and Development of Equipment/Clinic Planning/
Market Research in the Industry

Ann Gallant
Forum, Stirling Road, Chichester PO19 2EN, UK
Telex 86402, CHITYP. G, Ref Gallant

Ellison, Brindley Road South, Exhall Trading Estate,
Exhall, Coventry, UK Tel (0203) 362505

Esthetic and Beauty Supply, 16 Coldwater Road, Don Mills,
Ontario M3B 1Y7, Canada Tel (416) 444 1154
There is also a Californian office, USA

A NOTE ON BEAUTY EDUCATION INTERNATIONAL — BEAUTY CLUB

Beauty Club offers a unique service to the beauty industry; through COMMUNICATION, MOTIVATION and EDUCATION the club can provide all the necessary information for success in this exciting and profitable field; through its own Newsletter it keeps its members informed of all the latest developments in the industry around the world.

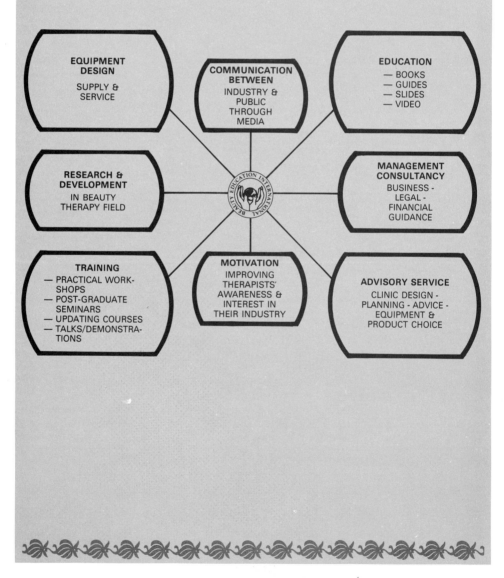